WILDLIFE
FACT·FILE
yearbook
·1993·

Overleaf: *A walrus'
tusks have many good
uses. They help it
clamber over ice, and
serve as duelling
weapons when males
fight for a mate.*

WILDLIFE
FACT·FILE
yearbook

·1993·

Foreword by
Jonathon
Porritt

Includes an
interview with

Gerald
Durrell

First published in the UK in 1992 by International Masters Publishers Ltd.
.Winchester House, 259–269 Old Marylebone Road, London, NW1 5RW

Edited, designed and produced by International Masters Publishers Ltd, London.

Publishing manager	*Deborah Clarke*
Editor	*John Birdsall*
Editorial consultant	*Jonathan Elphick*
Deputy editor	*Matthew Turner*
Sub-editor	*Amanda Coe*
Art editors	*Colin Hawes, Frank Landamore*
Designer	*Keith Davis*
Illustrator	*Steve Kingston*
Picture editor	*Mira Connolly*
Picture researchers	*Jackum Brown, Vickie Walters*
Senior production controller	*Suzie Hutton*
Production controller	*Stefan Podhorodecki*

Colour reproduction by Kestrel Lithographic Reproductions, Chelmsford, Essex
Printed and bound by Arnoldo Mondadori, Verona, Italy

Authenticators

Dr Pat Morris BSc PhD
Lecturer, Department of Biology, Royal Holloway and Bedford New College
Bob Scott
Head of Reserves Management, RSPB
Dr M A Taylor
Assistant Keeper of Earth Sciences, Leicestershire Museums Service

Set in 11/13pt Garamond

Every effort has been made to use environmentally friendly materials in the
production of this book. The paper contains 50 per cent recycled fibres and was pulped and
bleached using acid-free substances. Oxygen was used in the bleaching process, avoiding the
use of environmentally damaging chemicals. The boards were manufactured from
100 per cent recycled materials.

The publishers would like to thank Hal Robinson, Sydney Francis and Dr Tony Hare
for all their help and advice in producing this book.

ISBN: 0 9518566 1 8

CONTENTS

FOREWORD

For me, this yearbook is like a re-run of a lifetime's involvement in the natural world. I first tuned into nature as a young lad with an insatiable appetite for wildlife magazines, learning to identify all but the rarest of species without so much as a glance at the captions under the endless array of wonderful photos.

But when I came back to environmental matters in my early twenties, I found I'd moved on beyond straight natural history. What was the point of trying to save the blue whale or the lesser spotted owl if the economic policies that put them at risk in the first place remained unchanged?

But the bedrock is still the natural world, the multitude of different species with which we share this planet, the habitats and ecosystems on which we depend. Which is why books like the *Wildlife Fact-File Yearbook* have a power that reaches far beyond their wise and authoritative words. The stunning images shown here allow us to respond with joy, anger, amazement or sadness — and how many times must it be repeated that our emotions are a crucial part of efforts to protect the earth?

Of course we need the facts, but the facts on their own are rarely enough to persuade people (let alone governments) to change their ways. We must therefore learn again to feel at one with the earth, to trust our emotions, and to show reverence — not just respect — for the rest of life on earth.

Jonathon Porritt

Above: *The cause of conservation owes much to the work of Jonathon Porritt. For six years Director of Friends of the Earth, he is currently their Special Advisor.*

Left: *The dew of a summer morning frosts the fine hairs of a buff-tip moth caterpillar. The adult that finally leaves the pupa is patterned to look just like a chip of birch wood.*

7

INTRODUCTION

Another year brings another *Wildlife Fact-File Yearbook*. Once again, this unique book presents a fascinating and revealing insight into the natural world – from vital work aimed at reducing the threats facing bears and otters, to thrilling new discoveries about pterosaurs, the extraordinary winged reptiles that last flew about 65 million years ago.

Clear, vivid text and beautiful illustrations build on the solid bank of material contained in the *Wildlife Fact-File* to give you an up-to-the-minute picture of the world of wildlife — without repeating any of the information or images on the cards.

There are stunning photo-essays that explore the intriguing question of how animals move, focus on the gorgeously plumaged birds of paradise and their bizarre courtship displays, and reveal the secrets of life high in the rainforest canopy.

You will also have the privilege of entering the realm of the grey whale — the most primitive of all living whales — as well as the chance to step into the 'sixth dimension' and share new discoveries about the extraordinary senses possessed by many living creatures. There is also an in-depth examination of the world of falconry which explains how this traditional craft is playing an important part in the conservation of some of the most threatened birds of prey.

There are hard-hitting and revealing analyses of the effects of so-called 'green tourism', the impact of conservation programmes on indigenous peoples and the problems caused by the ever-increasing demands of modern fisheries. We also examine the severe drought of 1992 and its implications for Britain's wildlife, take a look at some of the problems facing the real-life paradise that is the Galapagos Islands and explore the ways in which high technology is being used to help study and protect marine wildlife.

The growing interest in wildlife gardening is celebrated in a season-by-season description of the many species that visit, and increasingly depend upon, our own back gardens. Then we take a trip beyond the beach to discover the remarkably rich undersea world off the British coast and how conservation organizations such as the Marine Conservation Society are fighting to protect it for the benefit of us all.

There are also revealing profiles of two of the most successful and best known pressure groups, the Royal Society for the Protection of Birds and Greenpeace, together with clear accounts of the essentials of international wildlife law and the impact of the reorganization of the Nature Conservancy Council, which cut through the jargon and spell out the hard facts.

There is a candid interview with the well-known author, TV personality and founder of the world-famous Jersey Wildlife Preservation Trust, Gerald Durrell, as well as revealing insights into the personal experiences of a wildlife warden in Africa and a wildlife sound recordist.

The Green Pages feature a calendar of events in the world of wildlife and the environment over the past year, together with details of forthcoming events in 1993. Other elements in this fact-packed section include updates of the features in last year's *Yearbook,* so that you can follow the stories through and keep abreast of the latest developments.

Whether read on its own or used alongside your collection of *Wildlife Fact-File* cards, this beautiful and informative book will prove indispensable in helping you appreciate and understand the amazing world of wildlife.

Far left: *The rainforests of Belize in Central America are home to the tiny red-eyed tree frog.*

ANIMALS OF THE WORLD

Life on earth began some one and a half million years ago, and during this unimaginable span, millions of species have evolved — some only to become extinct, and some which we have yet to discover. Among the most adaptable species are the bears, and this section opens with a look at the latest research on black and brown bears.

We also examine the remarkable senses that give many animals the edge necessary for survival, and look at the flamboyant birds of paradise and the tenacious grey whale, which has twice recovered from the brink of extinction. The perilous migrations of birds are explained, along with the mysterious ways in which animals move.

A sense of the past plays a part in the fascinating traditions and lore of falconry, and a more distant past comes to life in research into the pterosaurs, winged reptiles which ruled the skies long before modern birds. We end the section with a more contemporary look at efforts to restore the otter population in Britain, and offer a novel view of life in the world's rainforests: from high above the ground.

Above left: *The mountain gorilla's aggressive demeanour conceals a shy nature. This endangered mammal continues to suffer from the clearance of its habitat by humans.*

Above: *Successful conservation action has saved the red kite from extinction in Britain, but this beautiful bird of prey is still rare.*

Left: *The loggerhead turtle's huge flippers power it through the warm waters off the coast of Florida.*

BEAR ESSENTIALS

Above: *The awesome Kodiak bear of Alaska is the largest subspecies of the brown bear.*

Right: *Bears are the largest living land carnivores — but size does not guarantee survival, as researchers are discovering.*

Time is running out for the world's bears. The effects of habitat destruction and poaching threaten to eliminate many bear populations during the next 20–30 years. This bleak possibility created a solemn mood at the Ninth International Conference on Bear Research and Management held in Missoula, Montana, in February 1992. Over 400 biologists gathered to exchange ideas and the results of their latest research. But amid the thrill of sharing new insights there grew a worrying awareness that conditions, particularly for black and brown bears, are rapidly deteriorating.

To make conservation effective, a solid foundation of good research is essential, but black and brown bears are among the more difficult mammals to study. They are often found in remote locations living far apart, tend to be secretive by nature and are dormant during the winter when visibility is best and good tracking snow is present. What's more, when they are visible they are potentially dangerous. It isn't surprising therefore that the study of bears has lagged behind other areas of wildlife research.

Through the 1950s knowledge of bears was limited to the observations of naturalists and hunters and what could be deduced from droppings, signs and the carcases of dead animals. In the 1960s, however, scientists began to develop the tranquillizing drugs and radio telemetry equipment that have since revolutionized practical research. Over the last two decades the number of biologists armed with these new techniques and working on bears has greatly increased, resulting in a proliferation of research and publications. Unfortunately, the threats to bears and their habitats have grown far faster than our knowledge of how to diminish them.

Worldwide, six of the eight bear species are faring poorly — only the black bear and the polar bear are relatively secure. The brown bear, known in North America as the grizzly, is the most widely distributed species and, though doing well in certain places, is facing serious threats in other areas. Almost all bear research to date has been done on the black and brown bears of North America, and North American experts have helped start telemetry studies on brown bears in Spain, Sweden, Croatia and Mongolia.

Techniques to capture and tag bears are now routine, thanks to the pioneering efforts of many biologists. Early drugs were dangerous, both to bears and biologists. Doses were unreliable and bears would suddenly awaken during the radio collaring procedure — an alarming experience for bear and biologist alike! Drugs are now used with a wide safety margin that can tranquillize a bear in three to eight minutes and allow it to recover slowly after an hour.

In open terrain bears can be darted with a tranquillizing gun fired from a helicopter. Where thick cover and trees interfere, a bear can be trapped in a large barrel or a

Below: A researcher weighs a young cub taken from its winter den. The cub is returned to its mother unharmed and the data are recorded for future use.

culvert-style trap with a door triggered by the bear tugging at sacks of bait hung in the rear of the trap. The bear is safely held until it can be injected with a syringe on a pole.

Researchers examine, weigh, mark and radio-collar the immobilized bears before releasing them. Collared bears can be located and followed from the air using special radio receivers. Collar batteries last for over two years and by changing collars before the batteries wear out, it is possible to track individual bears for many years. This monitoring provides information on movements, habitat use, breeding, rate of reproduction and survival.

Permanent marks such as ear tags or tattoos can also generate useful information.

Above: *Teeth provide important information about a bear's age. Data can be taken from a live, immobilized bear — as here — or from the carcase of a dead animal.*

Left: *In areas which sustain remnant bear populations, the actual 'bear density' — measured as the number of bears per 500sq km, for example — may be very low.*

A female Kodiak bear killed last year by a hunter had been tagged as a youngster in 1958. This 35-year-old bear is the oldest wild bear yet documented. Unmarked bears can be aged by their teeth. A small premolar tooth, when extracted, sliced, and stained, reveals a series of lines like tree rings. These are called *cementum annuli* and correspond to the bear's age. Cementum studies suggest that bears in the wild normally live only into their 20s, and that females tend to outlive males.

In the early 1900s, biologists described dozens of species of grizzly bear in Alaska alone, sometimes basing their definitions on the discovery of a single skull. It is now generally accepted, however, that only one species of brown or grizzly bear, *Ursus arctos*, exists in North America, Europe, and Asia. Studies of undisturbed populations of brown bears in Alaska are using new DNA techniques to determine the extent of genetic variation within and between areas. This is important when trying to save small populations such as those in Europe. For there is a fear that among remnant populations of bears, inbreeding could make future generations less viable. These concerns have prompted biologists to consider introducing unrelated individuals into small populations to maintain genetic diversity.

Much research on both black and grizzly bears concentrates on habitat relationships, for the habitat contains all that is necessary

persists in the face of some habitat alteration there seems to be a threshold beyond which recovery is impossible. It is difficult to know what the threshold is or even when it has been passed, because individual bears may continue to live an area even after a viable population is lost. Human settlements often carve bear habitat up into smaller and smaller chunks until these can no longer support a bear population.

Uncontrolled killing by humans is also contributing to the demise of bears. Bears mature slowly, with females producing their first litters at six to eight years old. They then keep their offspring with them for two to four years. Even if they live to be 20 years old they may produce only a few litters in their lifetime, and cub mortality in the first year is high — typically 25–50 per cent. One Alaskan study that followed 11 female grizzlies from sexual maturity to their death found that each bear produced an average of only two surviving yearlings during its life. The projection of data from these kinds of studies into computer models has demonstrated how sensitive bear populations can be to mortality. Without over-

Above: *In North America the brown bear is known as the grizzly bear. This name refers to the silvery tips on the hairs of its coat.*

Right: *Bears use their considerable intelligence to develop hunting techniques. Individuals learn from experience which is the best position in a particular river from which to snatch fish.*

for the survival of bears in an area. Recent studies documenting the food habits and habitats of bears reveal an amazing adaptability. Because of climate and vegetation, brown bears in southeast Alaska depend on stands of old growth temperate rainforest, whereas other grizzlies in northern Alaska thrive hundreds of kilometres north of the treeline. Black bears throughout North America are closely tied to forested areas, yet new work done in Labrador has found black bears living on the treeless tundra, having moved into areas where grizzlies had been exterminated.

The adaptability of black and brown bears is cause for hope, but human activities do take their toll and the impact tends to be cumulative. Even if a bear population

hunting by humans there is not a problem, since bears evolved with few other enemies and natural mortality rates for mature animals are fairly low.

In another area of research, unravelling the mystery of bear hibernation remains a challenge. When biologists peer into black bear dens before immobilizing the animals, they are privileged to witness one of the most remarkable physiological feats in the mammal world. In these small, grass-lined chambers bears may spend six to eight months without eating, drinking, urinating or defecating, yet without significant loss of bone or muscle. Strictly speaking, a bear doesn't hibernate since its body temperature hardly drops and it can wake when disturbed as if it had only been asleep. Remarkably, bears in a dormant state detoxify and recycle metabolic waste and continue to build bone. How females combine hibernation and pregnancy is another mystery waiting to be investigated.

Recent work suggests that serum from hibernating bears injected into white rats and even monkeys can elicit a slight metabolic response. More work is needed, but

the possibility that other non-hibernators may possess receptors for the hibernation trigger is exciting. Other work on the medicinal properties of bear gall has resulted in the synthesis of a drug used to dissolve cholesterol gallstones. Physiologists are also trying to isolate the substances that allow bears to hibernate so successfully. Doctors are hopeful that breakthroughs in the treatment of kidney disease and osteoporosis may result from research now being conducted. Some scientists even feel that it will eventually be possible to induce a state akin to hibernation in humans taking part in extended space flights.

Every study of bear behaviour has demonstrated the extraordinary individuality, intelligence and adaptability of bears.

Above: *It is second nature for the inquisitive cubs to explore their environment. This is not a problem in a purely wild habitat, but in areas where humans visit or settle, dangerous encounters can occur.*

Far right: *Play is part of the learning behaviour of these endearing and complex mammals.*

Members of family groups exhibit distinct personalities and moods. Bear societies are organized around a pecking order that develops as bears in an area grow up and learn their relative status through play and fighting. Family groups, especially females with older offspring, are high-ranking.

The years the cubs spend with their mother represent an intense learning period. The cubs do not realize that their high status is a reflection of their mother's dominance, and are in for a rude awakening when the spring of their weaning arrives and the female no longer tolerates their presence. On their own for the first time, they are now at the very bottom of the pecking order. Young males almost always leave the area (probably to minimize inbreeding) and females remain where they are raised. These young, curious, insecure bears constantly explore and test their environment and are quick to take advantage of food or rubbish left by careless people. Many problem bears are these recently weaned young who become nuisances to humans and end up being shot.

On the conservation front there is cause for both concern and hope. Historically, either black or brown bears — or both — inhabited almost every habitat type in North America, while brown bears were found throughout Eurasia. Today, black bears have managed to hold on to more of their former range, though their populations are now more scattered and isolated. Grizzlies have lost 99 per cent of their range in the 48 adjoining states of the USA.

These small, isolated populations are extremely vulnerable to inbreeding, excessive mortality and extinction. Only in Alaska, northern Canada and the former Soviet Union do large tracts of intact grizzly habitat occur. Even in Canada, however, grizzlies have been eliminated from one quarter of their original range and are considered at risk in 63 per cent of their current range. The last strongholds of grizzly and black bears are vulnerable to increasing human populations, uncontrolled resource exploitation and climatic changes. Poaching of bears to provide the Far East with coveted paws and gall bladders is also a serious problem that continues to worsen.

The long-term conservation of bears will be a difficult and frustrating task. Dedicated biologists risk their lives every year working to gain the knowledge needed to attack the problems. Pay is low, the hours long, and the work dangerous. Despite this, many scientists are devoting their lives to the cause. They now have the benefits of hindsight from mistakes made elsewhere as well as recent research data and the advantage of sophisticated techniques. Economic and social pressures, however, often supersede environmental concerns. Nothing is more frustrating than the plight of biologists, handicapped by limited resources and funding, watching bears losing out yet again in the face of human encroachment.

Ideally we should be providing for the long-term conservation of bears where they

Below: *Black bears are marginally more successful than their brown relatives, thanks to a slightly higher rate of reproduction and a milder temperament.*

CAUGHT IN THE CROSSFIRE

The European brown bear has disappeared from much of its former range and is highly endangered in many of the areas where small populations still persist. Brown bears probably disappeared from Britain as early as the 10th century. Small remnant populations in France, Italy and Greece are barely hanging on. Romania, Scandinavia, Poland, Spain and Czechoslovakia have more secure populations, but there is no room for complacency.

What was formerly a success story in the former Yugoslav Republic demonstrates how quickly conditions can change. The recent outbreak of civil war throughout Croatia and Bosnia-Herzegovina has had

tragic human consequences, but has also devastated brown bear populations there. The war zone includes important National Parks where uncontrolled timber exploitation, fires, bombing and shooting of wildlife are all occurring. Scientific research has been suspended as a result of the conflict and income for wildlife management from the sale of hunting licences has stopped. Djuro Huber, a biologist from Croatia, has estimated that as many as two-thirds of Croatia's 250 brown bears could have been killed by the summer of 1992. The spread of fighting to Bosnia and Herzegovina has also resulted in a serious threat to the 800 bears that live there.

are still abundant rather than waiting until they are scarce. Recent work suggests the need for a series of large protected parks and wilderness areas with adjoining areas suitable for bears. Remnant populations demand protection and intense management, and the reintroduction of bears into suitable unoccupied habitat must also be explored. All these steps are necessary to ensure that our children don't inherit a world almost devoid of bears.

As the writer Aldo Leopold said: 'relegating grizzlies to Alaska is like relegating happiness to heaven; one may never get there'. A country with bears is immeasurably richer. No matter how many times you encounter a bear, it remains a thrilling and humbling experience.

John Hechtel

UNCOMMON SENSES

Above: *The feathery antennae of the male emperor moth enable it to detect a single airborne molecule of a distant female's scent.*

Far right: *Bechstein's bat bounces sound waves off the surface of the water to help it navigate accurately in darkness.*

Right: *We describe someone with keen eyesight as 'eagle-eyed', and with good cause. The golden eagle can spot small mammal prey from high in the air.*

Imagine being able to chart the oceans using the earth's magnetic field; to smell another creature half a kilometre away; to be able to approach it in darkness, yet adapt at once to bright light and see the target underwater from 15m away; and then to detect the minute electric fields produced by its muscles. These extraordinary sensory capabilities belong to the blue sharks of the North Atlantic. The female blue shark mates on the east coast of North America, but gives birth 4800km away in the sea off Portugal. On her journey, she is guided day and night by the earth's geomagnetic field — one of the few navigational cues available in an almost featureless sea.

Many other animals possess remarkable sensory abilities. Honed by millions of years of evolution, these faculties ensure that an animal navigates successfully, finds food, and attracts a partner.

The almost miraculous sense of direction possessed by many species has long perplexed naturalists and scientists alike. New evidence suggests that many animals possess a built-in magnetic sense. The key substance is magnetite, an iron-rich mineral which responds to the earth's magnetic field. In animals' bodies, particles of magnetite occur close to bunches of nerve cells.

In bees they are located in the abdomen, while in mammals and birds, magnetite is concentrated in the nose region. These tiny magnets twist to align themselves with the north or south magnetic poles, producing a torque that the nerve cells pick up. The presence of magnetite enables salamanders to return to their natal ponds, migrating birds to find their way back to their nest sites, sharks and whales to locate feeding and breeding grounds in the vast seas, and tuna to cross the oceans on regular routes.

Total reliance on a magnetic sense, however, also results in mass strandings of small whales such as pilot whales. In the midst of the sea, these ocean travellers can swim safely with all their other navigational senses 'switched off', guided only by the earth's geomagnetic field-lines or contours. As a result, a pod of whales may follow a magnetic contour over a sand-bar or a shelving beach and be taken by surprise. The animals activate their other senses, but often it is too late, and they become fatally stranded. Luckily, these strandings are rare.

Perhaps the best-studied navigational marvel is that of bird migration. Here, too, the magnetic sense plays a key role, but birds do not rely on just one guidance system. Those using regular flyways may recognize geographical landmarks such as mountains, lakes and rivers, while night-fliers may listen for biological landmarks, such as frogs croaking far below.

Birds generally navigate using the sun, moon or stars. To use the sun, however, a bird must be able to allow for its changing position. It is possible that by sensing fluctuations in the geomagnetic field a bird obtains a magnetic map of the world, by which it plots a course.

Some young migrants inherit, rather than learn, the directions in which they should

recognize others of its kind by the rate and pattern of the charges they emit.

Electricity is, in fact, produced by all animals — albeit in the tiniest of quantities — when their muscles and nerves are working. Some predators are able to sense this electrical activity and so are led to their next meal. Jelly-filled pits on a shark's snout, known as the ampullae of Lorenzini, can even detect the minute electric currents produced by a flatfish's beating heart. The hammerhead shark has ampullae spread across the front of its broad head, with which it scans the sea floor to find buried fish. The duck-billed platypus uses a similar sensor in its snout to probe the river bed for invertebrates.

Animals have exploited all the available sensory channels to increase their chances of finding food. Pits in the rattlesnake's snout detect the heat given off by prey. The hummingbird can see colours at the ultraviolet end of the light spectrum and follows lines on flower petals, invisible to humans, that guide it to the nectar. The cheetah has a horizontal strip of cells in the back of its eye that focus on targets silhouetted against the horizon. The four-eyed fish has each eye split into two in order to see above and below the water at the same time, while the kingfisher's lens system allows it to see well in the air, then change to underwater vision as it dives below the surface. The brown hyena, the wolf and the red fox all depend on a keen sense of smell to locate prey, while bat-eared foxes, as their name suggests, have extra-large ears with which they listen for termites underground.

Most bats use echo-location to track their airborne insect prey. A cruising bat might produce five or ten sound pulses per second — enough to help it navigate in the dark but insufficient for investigating a target. When it locates prey, however, the rate speeds up to 50 pulses per second, but as it closes in and needs to know precise

head. The most westerly population of European garden warblers, for example, are programmed to fly southwest in September to head for the Iberian Peninsula, southeast in October to fly from the Straits of Gibraltar to equatorial West Africa, and northeast the following April to return to Europe.

Fish, too, use some remarkable techniques to find their way around. The so-called weak electric fish, for example, surround themselves with an electrical field produced by strips of flattened muscle or nerve cells in their tail or the sides of their body. By sensing disturbances in this electrical field, a fish can move safely through even the most murky water and can even

details about its target, it increases the number of pulses to over 200 per second.

Some prey species, however, have evolved defences against bat sonar. The tiger moth, for example, can hear a bat's echo-location calls and so take evasive action by flying in loops and plummeting towards the ground. Tropical tiger moths can also jam the bat's sonar. The bat receives an echo from the moth, but just as it is diving at maximum speed, the moth fires a burst of sound at it. The bat is startled, and the moth escapes.

Attracting a mate may also involve the use of specialized senses: moths, for example, use an ultra-developed sense of smell. To attract a mate, the female wafts an attractive sex pheromone into the air which the male, using the 60,000 sensory hairs of his feathery antennae, can detect diluted down to a single molecule. Once he has detected about 200 molecules he will track the female down and mate with her. The bolas spider has, however, turned this communication system to its advantage. It drops a line of silk ending in a sticky ball and releases chemicals that resemble the pheromones of a female moth. Males attracted by the scent are then caught on the whirring lure.

A recent discovery of the natural world has been the love-call of the African elephant. This call comprises rumbles of such low frequency that they are inaudible to humans. Because the solitary males may be many kilometres from a receptive female, and she is ready to mate for only a few days every five years, the female needs to alert a mate to her condition — and low-frequency 'infra-sounds' carry farthest.

She calls for about 30 minutes, using the same sequence of repeated patterns. The bull also rumbles in reply, but on reaching the herd, he grows quiet and listens out for the female. After mating, she produces a special rumble which sends the rest of the herd into a frenzy. They rumble, trumpet and defecate in what researchers have called a 'mating pandemonium'.

For many years a mysterious, deep roar has been heard in the oceans of the world. The pulsed, low frequency sound was thought to come from a source such as surf crashing on the shore. But investigations have revealed that the sound is the product of the fin whale. Fin whales are seen travelling alone or in small pods, but these whales are probably part of a much larger herd whose members, perhaps a hundred kilometres apart, communicate with each other, using a 'sixth sense' which we are only just beginning to understand.

Michael Bright

Left: *This hibiscus flower may appear very different to the ruby-throated hummingbird, which sees colours invisible to human eyes.*

Below: *Heat-sensitive pits in this bushmaster snake's snout quickly alert it to the presence of warm-blooded prey.*

BIRDS OF THE GODS

Far right: *The Emperor of Germany's bird of paradise displays his impressive tail feathers in a shimmering spectacle of colour.*

High in the mountains of central New Guinea, the first rays of the rising sun filter through the leaf canopy of the humid, cloud-wrapped forest. Suddenly, a flash of electric blue lights up the sombre backdrop of the great trees. The fabulous male blue bird of paradise has arrived at his treetop display site to perform one of the most remarkable courtship rituals in the entire bird kingdom.

At first, he is difficult to distinguish in the gloom of the rainforest, since his body is mainly blackish. Then, in an instant, he swings his body backwards to hang upside-down from the moss-covered branch. He fans out his spray of shimmering purplish-blue feathers that cascade from either side of his breast, to create a psychedelic apron that contrasts startlingly with the spread of velvety-black and chestnut-red feathers higher on his breast. His two long, wire-like central tail feathers, which are black tipped with blue, encircle his body in a wide arc. Throughout the display, this fantastic creature sings a strange, metallic-sounding rhythmic song, which has been variously likened to the noise of an electric drill or that of an alien spacecraft, the sound throbbing in time with the pulsing of his sumptuous plumes.

There are 43 species of birds of paradise, most of which live in the wet forests of New Guinea, with four species in eastern Australia and two on the Molucca Islands (once known as the Spice Islands) in Indonesia. They range in size from birds little larger than a sparrow to some which are as big as a magpie. They are all stout, superficially crow- or starling-like birds, with rounded wings and large, powerful feet. Most species eat mainly fruit, but the bills of birds of paradise vary greatly, from those which are short and heavy and designed to deal with a varied diet, to the long, slender, downcurved bills of the riflebirds and sicklebills, which are specialist tools for winkling out insects from their homes.

But the most striking feature of this extraordinary family of birds is the stunning plumage of the males. In no other bird family do the males sport such a remarkable range of brilliant ornamental plumage: from breast shields, capes and cascading flank plumes to long, thin, wire-like feathers extending from the centre of the tail or even from the head. The males use this impressive array of finery in ritualized displays at regular sites. Here they parade in splendour to attract the watching females, which are dowdy and inconspicuous by comparison, with mainly brown and grey plumage, often barred underneath.

The display of the male superb bird of paradise is no less stunning than that of the blue bird of paradise. He expands his iridescent green breast shield and spreads his huge, bronze-black cape around his head

Below: *The crested bird of paradise is one of over 30 species which inhabit the steamy jungles of southeastern New Guinea.*

like some Elizabethan courtier's ruff. As he does so, he performs a little dance on his display perch — a large branch in the lower forest canopy — and displays the brilliant yellow inside of his bill as he utters harsh, screaming calls. Another, relatively little-known species is found only on two islands in the Moluccas group, and rejoices in the name of Wallace's standard-wing. The male of this species raises an iridescent green breast shield, whose feathers are greatly elongated at the sides, so that it stands out at right angles to his body. He also raises and lowers a pair of extremely long narrow, white plumes that extend from the bend of each wing and erects the feathers on the top of his head.

The male twelve-wired bird of paradise is a stunning black-and-yellow bird with a long bill. Selecting a high, exposed branch for his performance, he erects his black breast shield, which is edged with brilliant emerald green, into a large disc. From his flanks, 12 wire-thin feathers radiate in every direction. Males of this species have also been seen to whirl rapidly around a vertical branch, opening and closing their wings, in a frenzied performance which is accompanied by sharp metallic calls.

The black sicklebill, a magpie-sized bird, erects three pairs of fans from his breast, their deep black feathers scintillating with a violet and green gloss, so that they resemble outspread arms. The similar-looking brown sicklebill not only gives an equally captivating display but also has an extraordinary call that sounds like a burst of machine-gun fire. The plaintive, nasal calls of the ribbon-tailed astrapia, which resemble the croaking of a frog, are less dramatic, but the male makes up for his poor voice with his two astoundingly long white central tail feathers which can grow to almost four times the length of his body.

Several species of the six-wired bird of paradise, or parotia, display not high up in the trees but on 'courts' which they prepare on the ground, meticulously clearing the area of leaves, twigs and any other debris. Here, the male performs a ritualized dance, swinging his head about so that the six 'wires' that sprout from the sides of his head, each ending in an oval 'racket', spin about in all directions.

In contrast to the males of most birds of paradise, which are solitary, those of all but

Below: *Found only in extreme northeastern Australia, the male magnificent riflebird holds a territory all year round. He stands on a bough and shows off his lustrous breastplate in order to attract females.*

one of the *Paradisaea* species (known as the plumed birds of paradise) display communally. *Paradisaea* males have huge trains of colourful plumes extending from each side of the breast: red in the Raggiana bird of paradise, red, yellow and orange with cinnamon tips in the greater bird of paradise, and white and yellow in the Emperor of Germany's bird of paradise. They also have long central tail wires. They display in the treetops in groups of up to 20 birds, extending their wings, raising the flank plumes so that they cascade over the back, and even hanging upside-down from the display branch. At their long-established display sites, also known as arenas or leks, they compete to outperform one another and establish a dominance hierarchy that determines which males mate with the audience of females.

Why is there such a striking difference between the elaborately plumed and gaudy males and the relatively dull females? It is likely that in the first birds of paradise to evolve, the males had much plainer plumage, similar to that of the females, and took only one mate. There are several species alive today, such as the manucodes, the paradigallas and MacGregor's bird of paradise, that are still like this. But in much of the lush New Guinea rainforest, food — particularly fruit — is so plentiful that the female rarely needs the male to help her find and gather it. Released from this duty, the males were able to spend much of their time and energy on courtship displays that enabled them to mate with more than one female. Because these polygamous males produced more young than the monogamous males, their genes were transmitted to more chicks and there was a gradual tendency among the family for the males to evolve ever more elaborate and colourful display plumage.

Another reason for the development of this dandyism may have been the absence

of native predators on New Guinea, which enabled the males to display boldly without the fear of being snapped up. Today, however, birds of paradise are at risk — from people. But traditional hunting of birds of paradise by the indigenous population of New Guinea seems to have had relatively little effect on the numbers of most species, since it was for many years essentially self-regulated at sustainable

Above: *Slightly smaller than a starling, the king bird of paradise is the smallest of the bird of paradise family.*

and the blue bird of paradise, are starting to decline. Few of the polygamous species suffer unduly from hunting because the males, which take no part in caring for the offspring, take up to 10 years to become sexually mature and acquire their gorgeous plumes. So if a mature male is killed, there are plenty of young males ready to take his place. By contrast, monogamous species, such as MacGregor's bird of paradise (which, although lacking dramatic plumes, is often hunted for food), share the task of feeding and rearing the young, and their populations are therefore highly susceptible to hunting pressure.

But the hunting by indigenous populations pales into insignificance when compared to the heedless plunder of birds of paradise by nineteenth-century European settlers. In order to supply the colonial plume trade and decorate ladies' hats and garments, some 80,000 skins were exported each year from New Guinea to Europe and North America. The number was probably even higher in some years; 30,000 were sold in one year in London alone. At the turn of the century one German animal dealer regarded the blue bird of paradise as so beautiful that he dedicated it to the crown prince of Austria. Skins from this exotic-looking creature may have fetched as much as £40 each.

Fortunately, there was a great reaction against this sickening, wholesale slaughter in Europe, and the anti-plume trade movement in Britain produced what was to become the Royal Society for the Protection of Birds. By 1910, the British Parliament had passed a bill prohibiting the sale or exchange of bird of paradise plumes. In 1913 the US government banned the importation of all bird plumage, and Britain, Canada and Australia, together with the other Commonwealth colonies, soon followed suit. The demise of the plumage trade was further hastened by the outright

Above: *Wilson's bird of paradise is distinguished by the vivid blue patches of bare skin on the crown.*

Above right: *The crested bird of paradise is the only species to build a spherical roofed nest near to the ground.*

levels. As with many other wildlife conservation issues, the conservation of birds of paradise is intimately bound up with the needs and rights of local peoples.

The adoption, however, by the tribespeople of modern weapons in place of their traditional bows and arrows has led to the deaths of more birds — not just for their plumes but also for food; and some of the scarcer species, such as the black sicklebill

banning of the commercial killing of the birds in New Guinea by the Dutch in 1924.

Today, birds of paradise face the increasing — and far more serious — threat of habitat destruction. At present, for many species, the threat has yet to take effect, for New Guinea is one country where large areas of relatively undisturbed rainforest remain — but for how much longer? Already farmers have taken over considerable amounts of land, and the blue bird of paradise, for instance, which needs large tracts of undisturbed forest, is losing its habitat; at lower altitudes, it may also suffer through competition with the Raggiana bird of paradise, which can adapt to a wider range of habitats.

Let us hope that these worrying trends can be reversed, and that the programmes for conservation under way in New Guinea will preserve much of its pristine rainforest — and the fabulous birds of paradise which they contain — for future generations to marvel at.

Jonathan Elphick

CREATURES OF MYTH & SPLENDOUR

Birds of paradise have long been known to the tribespeople of New Guinea, who use the males' ornamental feathers for ceremonial purposes, especially in elaborate head-dresses and as currency (for example as wedding gifts). They were, however, virtually unknown in the West until the early seventeenth century, when explorers and merchants began to ship the feathers to Europe. The explorers did not see the living birds, and the skins they acquired had their wings and legs cut off to show off the gorgeous plumes to best advantage. The birds were also known by the people of the Molucca Islands as 'the birds of the gods', and these facts combined led to the belief that birds of paradise spent their entire lives in the air, feeding on air and dew, with no need for legs. The females were even thought to incubate their eggs in a hollow on the male's back as he flew along.

By the early nineteenth century, the truth about these amazing birds was gradually coming to light. The first naturalist to see them alive, in 1824, was the Frenchman Réné Lesson. Other naturalists soon followed, including Alfred Wallace, the great English naturalist and co-proposer with Darwin of the theory of evolution. He described several species and was the first to send back accurate reports of the males' bizarre displays. The first photographs of the birds displaying in the wild were not taken until 1957. Even today, details of the lives of some species are hardly known.

WHALE WATCHING

Above: *Some grey whales have started to respond positively to the presence of researchers, approaching their boats and seeking attention from them. Others, however, go out of their way to avoid humans.*

Right: *The grey whale is the most primitive of all living whales. It has remained virtually unchanged for millions of years, yet it has one of the largest and most sophisticated brains of any living animal.*

The California grey whale has proved itself to be one of the most astonishingly resilient of the earth's animals. Twice in the past 150 years the species has been hunted to near extinction, yet its recovery to pre-exploitation levels now seems assured. The history of the California grey is more closely linked to humans than that of any other whale, and so it is especially heartening that there are grounds for optimism about its revival.

The California grey whale population, as of spring 1992, stood at between 22,000 and 23,000 animals, and is increasing at a rate of just over three per cent a year. The main limit on population growth seems to be the capacity of their Arctic feeding grounds to support them: these can probably sustain 24,000 grey whales, roughly the number that migrate there in the summer months.

A yearly journey of nearly 20,000km dominates a grey whale's life. It feeds during the summer in the Bering, Chuckchi and Beaufort Seas in the high Arctic, then swims to the warm, protected waters of a few isolated lagoons in Baja California in winter, to mate and bear its young. The return migration to the Arctic begins in mid-February. Newly pregnant females leave first, followed by the males. Mothers with new offspring are the last to leave, sometimes remaining until late spring or early summer. By the end of March, the whale population in the lagoons is fairly minimal.

Apart from mother-calf pairs, grey whales migrate independently. However, because they follow a narrow route along the coast, they can give the impression of mass migration. Swimming along the coasts of

California, Oregon, Washington, British Columbia and Alaska, some individuals venture near the shore, where whale-watchers gather to enjoy the spectacle. Rounding the Alaska Peninsula through Unimak Pass, they reach the feeding grounds as the ice is receding. The journey — the longest migration of any mammal — takes from 95 to 100 days.

Grey whales feed in the rich Arctic waters until the weather cools. A whale gains tonnes of weight during these summer months, padding its body with blubber up to 25cm thick. This fatty material both protects the whale from heat loss in the frigid Arctic waters and serves as an energy store to sustain it throughout migration. The whale feeds little during the rest of the year because feeding is strenuous, and it must have access to an abundance of food for the effort to be worthwhile.

In September and early October pregnant females begin to head south, followed shortly by other females, males and juveniles. They take the same route that they use when travelling north, but move faster, because of their abundant food reserves and the urgency of arriving at the lagoons. Juveniles tend to stop along the way, exploring islands and playing in kelp beds.

January sees the first whales reaching the lagoons and countless coves, bays, and inlets of Baja California. A few individuals round the tip of the Baja Peninsula into the Gulf of California, and some venture on to the coastal waters off mainland Mexico. By February, the lagoons are alive with whales.

Most grey whales mate in the lagoons. The act itself is elaborate. It usually starts in the morning, with males circling and thrusting their head clear of the water, breaching and splashing, attracting attention and pursuing females. Groups divide into trios as a female approaches one of the males, touching him with her flippers, and bringing her belly towards his. A male ready to copulate needs another male to give extra bodily support to ensure he can penetrate his mate. The three whales stay together for two hours or more, with repeated brief penetrations before the climax.

From the shore, watchers rarely see a grey whale at all: it is the spout or blow that catches the eye. Rising up to 4.5m above the surface of the water, this spout is a column of air, condensation and water droplets expelled from the whale's twin blowholes. On a still day, the blow can be heard a kilometre away or more, but on a windy day one may be unable to see or hear the spout at all.

Away from the shore, researchers take small boats or inflatables among mating and nursing whales, photographing their markings to identify and record individuals. Research has taken place for 30 years, but it was not until the 1970s that grey whales began approaching boats and soliciting

physical contact from people. In the 1980s this behaviour began to spread to other lagoons, and although still uncommon, it is astounding that it occurs at all.

More typical, however, is the response of migrating whales. The more people try to get near the whales, the more the whales stay offshore. They also tend to blow beneath the water to avoid being detected, and change direction under the surface to throw watchers off their track. None of this behaviour occurs when a grey whale is not being shadowed.

This response to humans is unsurprising: generations of aboriginal peoples have hunted whales. The grey whale, because of its predictability and seasonal proximity to land, was especially targeted by the people of Asia, Europe, and America. But as long as hunting technology remained primitive, the grey whale continued to thrive.

In the sixteenth century, however, subsistence hunting began to evolve into a commercial industry. The Basques were the first to supply the market with whale products through their huge Atlantic whaling fleet, and the Japanese were the most prolific whalers in the Pacific.

By the nineteenth century, Yankee and

Below: *A mother and calf play together in the warm waters of a Mexican lagoon.*

western European whalers were sailing the oceans to find these floating fortunes. In the 1840s whalers discovered the California grey whale's coastal migration, and set up whaling stations along its route.

A few years later the California grey whale was thought to be extinct and the whaling stations closed. The reprieve was brief, however. Early in this century the combination of steam-powered whalers and exploding harpoons once again made grey whale hunting a lucrative business. The partly rejuvenated stock, numbering some 15,000 or more animals, once more came under attack.

After the second onslaught against them, the population of California grey whales was reduced to less than 3000, yet still they were hunted. Finally, in 1946, the newly-formed International Whaling Commission (IWC) ratified the International Convention for the Regulation of Whaling. The new treaty forbade the killing of grey whales except by aborigines or by contracting governments when the products were for the express use of local aborigines. On the whole, the regulations have been effective.

The coastal migration and concentrated wintering grounds that once made the California grey whale susceptible to exploitation are now working to its advantage. The species' high reproductive rate, lack of natural predators, low mortality rate, and a fairly uncompromised food source have all enabled a recovery that seems miraculous. It has been so successful that

Below: *The blow is an awe-inspiring sight and, from a distance, may be the only tell-tale sign of a grey whale's presence.*

Left: *An international team of rescuers come to the aid of a grey whale trapped in ice. As the weather worsens, greys that are late in setting out for southern breeding grounds run the risk of becoming trapped in this way and dying as a result.*

in 1978 the US National Marine Fisheries Service down-listed the California stock from endangered to sustained management status. In 1991 they began proceedings to have it de-listed altogether.

Today whale-watching has replaced whale-killing as a significant industry. Along the west coast of North America people pay to see living whales and to marvel at the magnificence of these giant sea creatures. Nevertheless, some threats remain.

A migrating grey whale may run into the gill nets that commercial fisheries use along the Pacific coast. In 1988 gill nets were outlawed along much of the California coast but some are still in use, and the occasional whale dies as a result of entanglement.

The IWC also continues to set non-commercial quotas, and in recent years whalers from the former Soviet Union have killed 167 grey whales annually in the name of their aborigines. Despite recent political changes in this area it is likely that this killing will continue.

With the spread of seismic exploration for gas and oil reserves, some migrating greys now avoid exploration areas and,

more seriously, have abandoned affected feeding and wintering grounds. This may be threatening if Mexico decides to exploit reserves in the mating and calving lagoons. The USA and Canada are also increasing oil and gas exploration and production in the feeding areas. A major oil spill in feeding or calving areas could have a disastrous effect on the grey whales. Statistically the US government considers this risk to be minimal, but the *Exxon Valdez* disaster gives reason to question their complacency.

Despite anxiety about these potential dangers, the wonderful reality is that, at the beginning of the 1990s, the recovery of the California grey whale is nothing less than spectacular. As we increase our knowledge and understanding about the grey whale and its revival, the lessons learned may assist the recovery of other species. We may also hope that by taking time to watch these whales, we will come to appreciate the advantages of being surrounded by such awesome and beautiful creatures, and therefore may find it easier to temper our appetites so as not to endanger them again.

Jeff Hall

Below: *The migrating grey whale stays in waters less than 200m deep. Adept at navigating in relatively shallow water, the grey is not susceptible to the live strandings that afflict other species.*

FLYING INTO TROUBLE

Above: *An exhausted crossbill rests on Orkney after a long migration from Scandinavia.*

Far right: *A typical autumn day in Britain — or is it? These swallows are in fact gathering in South Africa, ready for the spring flight north.*

Below: *In Hungary, 2500 artificial nest pylons have been erected for the white stork.*

There are few more awe-inspiring feats in the natural world than the journeys made by migratory birds. These tiny scraps of life make annual journeys over deserts, mountains and oceans between their breeding quarters in the northern hemisphere and their tropical winter homes. Each year, some 5000 million landbirds travel from Europe and northern Asia to Africa alone, braving natural hazards from storms and starvation to birds of prey.

These natural threats have little impact on the huge flocks involved, but increasingly the migrants are having to cope with changes in the environment wrought by rising human populations. They face the loss of forests, wetlands and grasslands, the effects of pollutants, collision with man-made structures, and hunting.

It is becoming ever more urgent to discover more about migrants' needs. This is vital not only to help save the birds, but also because they serve as early indicators of impending environmental disasters.

A striking example of this began back in the late 1960s, and involved a little warbler called the whitethroat. Analysis of the Common Birds Census in Britain for the year 1969 showed a sudden dearth of this migrant in its hedgerow nesting habitat: numbers had slumped by a staggering 71 per cent between 1968 and 1969. The trend was mirrored across western Europe.

The cause was traced to the savannah and grasslands of the western Sahel region, on the southern borders of the Sahara, where the warblers spend the winter. In summer 1968, the rains failed and the resulting drought, intensified by desertification, wiped out many of the whitethroats. Numbers have remained low ever since, although there has been a recent increase due to improved rainfall in the Sahel.

It is not just songbirds that depend on events in Africa. The white stork is in trouble both in its African wintering quarters and in its European breeding range. The combined effects of drought in the Sudan and Sahel and irrigation schemes deprive the storks of their wet grassland feeding sites. Locust eradication in West Africa has also depleted a major food source.

When the storks fly north in spring to breed in Europe, they arrive in a landscape that has undergone radical changes over the past 40 years. Wet meadows and rough pastures have been drained and ploughed to grow high-yield crops, greatly reducing the numbers of the storks' prey, such as voles, frogs and grasshoppers.

In Sweden, Denmark, Germany, Austria and Switzerland, about 80 per cent of storks have been lost since 1900. Casualties in Spain have been particularly high. The birds are also faring poorly in Eastern Europe, due to damage caused by agricultural changes and political upheaval.

Above: *The Dalmatian pelican is one of many migrant species shot purely for sport in the Mediterranean region.*

Traditional nest sites on buildings are disappearing; new roof designs do not suit the bulky stick nests, and repair work on church spires and electricity pylons ruins nests or causes birds to desert. Overhead cables kill many of these large birds, especially the inexperienced young.

Some 6000 storks are shot each year by hunters as they pass through Syria and Lebanon, affecting populations breeding in eastern Europe and southwest Asia. Some 2000–3000 eastern white storks die in other wintering areas. Several thousand of the population breeding in western Europe are killed on migration and in winter, chiefly in the Niger wetlands and in northern Nigeria.

The slaughter of migrant birds is rife in many Mediterranean countries. About 10 million shooters and a million trappers kill an estimated 1000 million birds annually, ranging from tiny warblers to pelicans and eagles. Heavy hunting in restricted areas, such as islands, small estuaries or marshes, not only kills many birds but also disturbs the other birds in the area. This can have serious implications if the site is a crucial stopover point for long-distance migrants.

Wetland migratory birds are particularly at risk from habitat destruction. Cranes, geese and waders gather in huge numbers to pause for rest and food at relatively few stopover sites. Almost the entire Pacific coast populations of Western sandpipers and dunlin rely on the stopover site at the Copper River Delta in southeast Alaska, while some 80 per cent of red knots migrating along the east coast of the USA depend on the rich harvest of horseshoe crab eggs in Delaware Bay. Red knots and sanderlings are diminishing, with resort development and beach erosion threatening areas of Delaware Bay, and the risk of oil spills at other vital points on their route. Oil pollution also afflicts seabirds on their long ocean wanderings. Fishing can rob them of their food, and leaves deadly snares in the form of loose sections of netting.

North American migrant songbirds are essentially tropical species that spend the spring and summer up north, where they can exploit the seasonal bounty of insect food. They need extensive tracts of mature forest in both northern and southern habitats. The yellow-throated vireo, Acadian flycatcher, Swainson's warbler, hooded warbler, wood thrush and American redstart are all declining alarmingly. Their northern breeding forests are being cleared for timber, agriculture or development, and the fragmented remnants are less suitable for breeding. The cleared areas attract nest predators such as blue jays, racoons and cats, as well as cowbirds, which, like the European cuckoo, lay their eggs in songbirds' nests at the host family's expense.

The North American migrants are also losing their tropical forest winter habitat, as the rapidly growing human population satisfies its needs for living space, food, fuel and work. The countries worst hit include Jamaica and the Dominican Republic, and there is virtually no natural forest left in Haiti and El Salvador. Cuba, Guatemala and Honduras are not far behind. In Costa Rica, the remaining tropical forests will disappear within 30 years at present rates of destruction — and the birds with them.

Although a great deal of time and effort

is put into ringing and radio-tagging, site censuses and other research into migratory birds, we still know far too little. Protection of migrants is particularly complex, because many different habitats and countries may be involved, requiring detailed programmes of research and conservation. But it is vital to learn from the birds themselves and transcend national boundaries to coordinate protection measures, or many of our best-loved and most familiar migrant birds will some day leave our shores never to return.

Jonathan Elphick

Above: *Barnacle geese rely on a select few stopover points where they can recuperate during migration.*

Below: *The tiny Cape May warbler heads north each spring from the West Indies to the northern USA and Canada. This epic journey can total more than 5000km.*

ANIMALS IN MOTION

Above: *The long and muscular hind legs of the grasshopper enable it to leap high in relation to its size. The key to its power is resilin, a rubbery protein.*

Right: *The basilisk lizard derives its alternative name of Jesus lizard from an ability to 'walk on water'. In fact, it must run to stay on the surface, and can only manage this feat over short distances.*

From the fluttering butterfly to the bounding kangaroo, all animals are to some extent defined by the way they move. The ability to move — whether a few millimetres or from one end of the earth to the other — enables animals to find food, hunt prey, escape predators, seek out mates, colonize new areas and take shelter.

Since water comprises the largest habitat on earth, it is not surprising that an enormous diversity of species move by swimming. For microscopic creatures, water is sticky, and they need a lot of power to move through it. Many of these tiny animals have flagella — tiny, hair-like structures that beat with a wave-like motion to push the water backwards and sideways.

Some small organisms, such as the larvae of many marine snails, worms and starfish, have bands of shorter hairs called cilia. Each cilium straightens as it beats against the water, then bends on the return stroke, offering minimal resistance to the water.

Larger and faster animals rely on muscles for movement. Muscles are made up of proteins that stretch and contract. In its resting position a muscle is usually fully extended, and needs energy to contract.

Simple, soft-bodied animals such as flatworms and sea hares bend their body by contracting certain muscles while relaxing others. They swim with graceful undulations. The hydra uses muscles to bend to one side, shrink and extend its body and wave its tentacles.

Opposing sets of muscles are used for more complex movements. The earthworm has bands of circular muscles around its body which squeeze it into a long, thin

Right: *The cheetah reaches speeds of nearly 100km/h in pursuit of prey. However, it can only run at such a pace for about 400m, before it must stop to recover its breath and cool down.*

shape, while contracting strips of longitudinal muscles make it short and fat. Tiny bristles, called chaetae, on its underside anchor the worm on irregularities in the soil as it pulls its body forward. A jellyfish propels itself through the water by jet propulsion. As circular muscles in its bell contract, water shoots out backwards and powers the animal forward.

For more powerful and effective locomotion, the muscles need something rigid against which to work. The arthropods — the crustaceans, insects and their relatives — have an exoskeleton or rigid outer shell. They were probably the first animals to have specialized limbs for swimming and walking. In arthropod limbs the exoskeleton is jointed to allow complex movements.

In arthropod limbs, pairs of muscles are attached across the joints to work in opposite directions. This process, in which one muscle contracts to bend the limb and the other straightens it, is also found in the more advanced vertebrates.

The evolution of muscle blocks pulling against rigid bones enabled early fish to move fast and become successful predators. Most fish swim by flexing their body, fins and tail in a wave-like motion to displace water. The fins are used for steering, braking, stabilizing and propulsion. Only a few species, such as the boxfish and the seahorse, are so heavily armoured that they rely entirely on their fins for movement.

The streamlined body of a typical fish reduces its drag, and overlapping scales, thickly coated in slime, also help cut down resistance. The greatest streamlining is found in fast-swimming fish such as tuna and mackerel, but the speed record is held by the ocean-going sailfish, which can swim at up to 109km/h in short bursts.

their buoyancy. In some primitive species the swim bladder connects to the mouth, and probably evolved from a rudimentary lung, but in most the bladder is self-contained and the gas is produced by chemical processes. The fish secretes or reabsorbs gas to adjust its density as it changes depth.

Movement on land presents a whole new set of challenges. The drag created by friction with the ground makes it profitable to lift the body above the surface, but for this, gravity must be overcome and the body's weight must be supported by strong limbs.

The key to walking and running is balance. Arthropods, with many legs and a body close to the ground, have little problem. But with four legs, balance requires great control. For a dog, walking is easy, but as it speeds up, only two legs are on the ground at a time. If it gallops, there may be only one leg on the ground at any one time or even all four legs off the ground. The dog maintains balance because its steps follow each other so quickly.

Below: *The southern stingray's anatomy may seem crudely adapted for movement, but it 'flies' swiftly through the water, propelled by its wing-like fins.*

The legs of marine mammals have become modified to form flippers or paddles and, in the case of the whales and dolphins, are assisted by muscular tail flukes. Whales, dolphins and many seals undulate their body up and down instead of from side to side as they swim.

Since all living matter is denser than water, swimming animals need to achieve buoyancy. Microscopic floating organisms have long spines to increase their surface area-to-volume ratio, but in mobile animals this would increase drag. Some animals avoid sinking by swimming all the time. Water beetles trap a 'float' of air under bristles on their belly, and some sea slugs gulp air at the surface. Squid, sharks and a few other fish use lateral fins to generate lift, but they need to keep moving or else they sink.

Most fish, however, have a gas-filled swim bladder which they use to control

*Above: **The impala's bounding run helps it escape predators. By leaping high it reduces its contact with the ground, minimizing friction which would slow it down.***

Fast-moving animals such as gazelles and cheetahs have long legs to help thrust them off the ground for longer, reducing friction. The cheetah also has an extremely flexible spine, enabling it to swing its hind legs forward in front of its forelegs while galloping at speeds of up to 96km/h.

Tendons greatly enhance the thrust of limb against ground. Made of elastic material, they attach muscle firmly to bone. The Achilles tendon at the back of the heel is particularly important to mammals. As the foot touches down, the muscle and tendon relax, storing energy. This energy is released, spring-like, as the foot pushes off from the ground. Kangaroos and horses have particularly powerful tendons, which also cushion the impact of landing at speed. Storage of energy in elastic material is also the secret of the flea's jump, the grasshopper's leap and the power of insect flight.

Perhaps the strangest skeletal adaptation is that of the snakes, which have evolved without limbs. Most snakes rely on friction against the ground in order to move, and to do this they throw the body into a series of curves. On the outer part of the curve, the body presses against irregularities in the ground, much as an eel pushes against the

*Right: **The boa's sinuous movement is the result of friction between the snake's body and the surface it moves over.***

water, to obtain thrust. This method also works in underground tunnels, and some snakes use a similar technique to climb trees, pressing against ridges in the bark. A few species of snake, such as the puff adder, travel forward in a straight line. They have specially hinged scales which can be raised and lowered by means of muscles to push against bumps in the ground.

Some animals have developed the ability to leave the ground completely and move through the air. True flight is a complex process. Bats have membranes of skin stretched between greatly elongated fingers, and their wrist bones are fused to provide a strong anchorage for the muscles. But they lack the tail feathers of birds, which are useful in braking and turning.

In cross-section a bird's wing has a concave lower surface, and its curved leading edge tapers to a thinner trailing edge. In flight, air passing over the wing travels farther than air below it. It therefore travels faster, reducing pressure above the wing. The opposite happens below the wing, and this pressure difference generates lift.

The downbeat of the wing presses down and back against the air, with the feathers spread to create the largest possible surface. On the upbeat, the wing is folded slightly and the feathers compressed to minimize drag. Each of the main flight feathers can twist slightly, so that the wing is, in effect, made up of a series of small propellers which further aid flight. The body feathers streamline the bird's outline, while the tail feathers can serve as a rudder or as a brake.

At low speeds, turbulence is a problem, especially around the edges of the wing. To combat this, slow-flying or gliding birds can usually part the primary feathers to form slots that allow air to pass through. And by flying in V-shaped skeins, migrating geese may exploit each other's slipstreams.

To avoid stalling on landing, a bird brings its alula, or bastard wing, into play: this

works a little like the flaps of an aircraft. Spreading the tail feathers and angling the wings in order to brake is a familiar sight to anyone who has watched pigeons landing in a crowded city square. A similar technique is used by hovering birds such as kestrels to reduce their forward thrust.

The true hoverers are the hummingbirds, whose wings describe a figure-of-eight to allow them to remain in the same position as they feed from flowers. They are the only birds that can fly forwards, backwards and sideways. Some hummingbirds can beat their wings up to 50 times a second. Their high-sugar nectar food provides the energy necessary for such a strenuous lifestyle.

Birds use many techniques to save energy while flying. Small birds often have a dipping flight, flapping their wings to generate momentum, then gliding down briefly before the next flap. Many large birds seek out rising air currents or thermals, and spiral upwards on them, wings

Above: *This sequence of a leafhopper taking off shows how it streamlines its body to reduce drag in the initial stages. Once it is airborne, wing power takes over.*

spread wide. They may rise to heights of over 2000m before coasting down, often travelling several kilometres without needing to flap their wings. Seabirds also use the rising air currents found as the onshore wind sweeps over cliffs and headlands. Soaring birds such as vultures and eagles usually have long, strong wings, with widespread primary feathers to give added lift.

Swooping and diving require the opposite approach — the body needs to fall through the air like a stone. The peregrine falcon folds its wings close to its body as it plunges earthward, and there are claims that stooping peregrines have reached speeds of almost 400km/h. Brown pelicans, boobies and gannets assume a similar shape as they plunge into the waves.

Insects have flown for some 100 million years. Most adult insects have two pairs of wings attached to the thorax, although in the beetles one pair has hardened into elytra, or wing covers. The oldest flying insects are the dragonflies, and they are remarkable in that their two pairs of wings can operate quite independently of each

Right: *The dormouse's body is not particularly well adapted for leaping, since it has frail legs and a weighty torso. However, it is capable of jumping if absolutely necessary.*

Left: *As a member of the beetle family, the ladybird has only one pair of wings. The other pair have evolved into elytra — cases which cover the functional wings when the insect is not in flight.*

other. Each wing moves at an angle to the body, first downwards and forwards, then upwards and backwards. This helps to reduce drag and increase lift.

The wings of dragonflies, locusts and butterflies are attached to the thorax through slots in its sides. The main flight muscles join the bottom of the thorax. The wings pivot on the thorax wall, acting as levers which produce a large wing movement for a relatively small muscle contraction initiated by a nerve impulse.

Dragonfly wings beat at about 20 beats a second. This is slow by insect standards — bees flap their wings 180 times a second, and mosquitoes 600 times a second. Such rapid wingbeats cannot be triggered by individual nerve impulses. Instead, faster wingbeats use a different action. The wings are attached directly to the thorax, and the flight muscles are attached to the top and bottom of the thorax. As the flight muscles contract and relax, the wings are moved up and down. These muscles are of a special type that can produce about 40 wingbeats for every nerve impulse. These wingbeats also make use of the sudden release of energy stored in the rubbery protein resilin, just like the jumping flea.

The immense diversity of animal locomotion calls for a great input of sensory information to each animal's brain. Height,

Left: *The widely spread outer flight feathers of the white-backed vulture help it to soar on air currents for hours with little muscular effort. This is essential to its habit of scavenging carrion, which it spots from high in the air.*

speed, direction, balance and the various limbs all must coordinate, and the brain needs to interpret the changing scene viewed by the eyes. In more advanced animals, subtle control of movement involves information from stretch sensors in the muscles and the movements of fluid in the semicircular canals of the vertebrate ear which maintain stability and achieve movement. Hand in hand with the development of such complexity has gone evolution itself — through being able to move from one place to another, animals from widely separated locations can come together to mate and breed, thus enhancing genetic variation and the potential for further evolutionary changes.

Jill Bailey

A BIRD IN THE HAND

Falconry is a sport with a rich and fascinating history. In decline in the nineteenth century, it has regained popularity since World War II and is now flourishing among dedicated followers throughout the world. As well as providing recreation for those who practise it, falconry has played an important role in conserving some endangered species of birds of prey.

The first depictions of people with large birds on their wrist come from the Far East, on materials dated around 2000 BC. The sport has a long tradition in Britain, and in mediaeval times falconry enjoyed the popularity that a sport such as cricket has today. *The Boke of St Albans* prescribed the types of bird suitable for those in different walks of life, such as the gyr falcon (for royalty) and the goshawk (for a yeoman). Soldiers returning from the Crusades brought home new training techniques from the Middle East, where hawking had been popular for many centuries. The prominence falconry once had in British life is reflected in the number of words it has given to the language: 'booze', 'cadge' and 'hawker' are all words with their origin in falconry.

Traditionally, falconers divide the birds they fly into three groups: longwings, shortwings and broadwings. Each differs in shape, temperament and style of hunting. The longwings are the true falcons of the group *Falco*. They have relatively long, narrow wings which come to a point, and their bill has a notch in its upper edge which delivers a fatal bite.

Longwings are comparatively placid and easy to tame. The kestrel is a popular species for beginners, while the merlin was

Above: *Eagles are not widely trained for falconry, as they are heavy birds to carry on the fist, but their soaring flight makes them attractive to some specialists.*

once considered a 'ladies' bird'. The larger falcons, such as the peregrine, are capable of breathtaking flights. They may 'mount' to a 'pitch' of 100–300m, then 'stoop' on grouse or partridge which have been flushed by the falconer or his dog. Other large falcons, such as saker and gyr falcons, are not so suitable for this kind of flight, as they frequently take their prey by attacking it on the ground.

Confusingly, falconers use the word 'hawk' to refer to all trained birds of prey. True hawks of the genus *Accipiter* are known as shortwings. Typical shortwings,

such as goshawks and sparrowhawks, have shorter and wider wings than falcons. These, combined with their long tail, give them great agility in the air. In the wild, shortwings hunt mainly from perches, so trained birds are often slipped straight from their trainer's fist, to dash and weave after prey as it twists through cover. A shortwing may crash into a bush to seize a rabbit or pheasant with its relatively long legs, delivering the death blow with its talons. These birds are not for beginners, as they are not easily tamed, or 'manned' and they remain rather temperamental despite training.

Eagles, buzzards and related species have even deeper wings — hence their collective name of broadwings. These wings fit them for soaring flight. The Harris hawks and red-tailed hawks of North America are really buzzards, but can be skilful hunters and have become popular among falconers. Eagles are mostly too heavy to be popular. As a group, broadwings are more placid than the true hawks. They are quite easy to breed in enclosures, yet can take birds from pheasant to small waterfowl, and mammals from hare to squirrel.

A trained hawk takes less prey than a wild hawk, or a domestic cat in the country. Furthermore, a gun provides more game for the pot, so it is not surprising that falconry declined in Europe when guns became more reliable. Nevertheless, a succession of small clubs kept the skills alive in Britain. Falconry clubs were re-established in other European countries during the first half of this century, and the sport was introduced into North America. During the 1960s there was something of a falconry renaissance, perhaps stimulated by the growing general interest in wildlife.

Today, there are over a thousand falconers in Britain, Germany and the USA, with several hundred more throughout Western Europe, Canada, New Zealand and southern Africa. There are probably at least as many again in Middle Eastern countries, Turkey, the Indian subcontinent and southern parts of the former Soviet Union. Many national clubs make contact and cooperate with each other through the International Association of Falconry and of the Convention on Conservation of Birds of Prey.

Before World War II, few birds of prey were protected by law. Falconers traditionally took their birds from nests, as 'eyeasses', or trapped them in their first autumn, as 'passagers'. Adult raptors are long-lived, yet most species used in falconry have from two to four young in a nest each year. This surplus meant that many trained hawks were traditionally 'hacked back' to the wild. Other hawks simply returned to the wild after being lost while hunting. In Britain, goshawks were released to re-establish a wild stock which had become extinct in the nineteenth century.

Today, Eastern falconers continue to trap and release hawks in this way, as they have for centuries. In the West, however, falconry practices have been radically affected by the farm chemicals which almost wiped out some raptor populations in the 1950s and 1960s. The insecticide DDT stopped peregrines breeding successfully, and dieldrin killed many birds. As a result, Western falconers were no longer allowed to take hawks from the wild without a licence, just as interest in falconry was starting up again.

These restrictions led to high prices being offered for birds of prey and to some birds being taken without licences. In Denmark, where DDT had almost wiped out the

Above: *This falconer is wearing a 'cadge' — a frame which supports several hawks.*

Left: *The kestrel's hood prevents it from spotting prey and becoming agitated before the falconer has released it from the fist.*

Above: *This peregrine is launched after grouse in the north of England. Peregrine populations in other countries were re-established by falconers.*

Right: *Broadwings such as the buzzard are flown after prey that varies from pheasants to squirrels.*

any time since records began, and falconers have helped in many wild bird studies.

Today, British falconers must breed their own birds, and every bird must have a licence. Very few licences are given for wild birds of prey and only a few wild hawks and falcons are taken illegally — with harsh penalties for the poachers if they are caught. Raptors whose populations have been declining in Britain, such as harriers and barn owls, are not used at all for falconry. The British example shows that, with proper controls, raptor populations can thrive alongside large numbers of falconers. There is still considerable debate, however, over whether falconers contribute effectively to raptor conservation if, like pigeon fanciers, they are divorced from wild birds.

entire peregrine population, ruthless hawk dealers took young from the last surviving pair of these birds. In view of such behaviour, it is hardly surprising that bird protectors started campaigns to ban falconry.

Yet despite condemnation from conservationists during the pesticide era, many falconers started using the knowledge they had acquired through the sport as part of conservation projects. The restriction on wild birds led falconers to breed birds of prey in enclosures. This had previously been thought impossible, but enough birds were bred under these conditions for release schemes to be instigated. Falconers such as Professors Tom Cade and Christian Saar knew the best conditions in which to release raptors and ensure their survival in the wild, and were responsible for re-establishing peregrines in parts of North America and Germany. Falconers have also run a successful project to save the Mauritius kestrel, and species they are currently helping to rescue include the California condor and Philippine eagle. In Britain, the wild peregrine population is now higher than at

Countries such as the USA and Zimbabwe have another approach. Those who qualify for a falconry licence are allowed one or two wild birds a year, of a species which is abundant. In these countries, falconers still do much of the field work on wild birds of prey.

After a difficult period, falconers are becoming accepted again among conservationists. Unfortunately, birds of prey remain at risk in many parts of the world. Damaging pesticides are still used in developing countries, and habitat loss is the most serious threat of all. Raptor stocks can recover from pollution and persecution if steps are taken in time. This is the challenge which falconers have the skills to meet: helping raptors to survive in the future.

Dr R E Kenward

TRAINING A BIRD OF PREY

Training a bird of prey can be divided into three stages. First is the manning process, during which the hawk learns to trust the falconer and then becomes accustomed to the other sights and sounds of the human world. The falconer makes all introductions gradually, while the bird feeds on the fist.

In the 'calling off' stage, the hawk learns to fly to the fist for food. A light line, the creance, is initially attached to leather straps, called jesses, on the hawk's legs. The lure, a token prey with meat attached, is also introduced at this stage. The falconer later swings the lure in the air for free-flying longwings to chase, as a way of improving their flight skills.

In the third stage, the hawk is 'entered' — released to fly after suitable quarry. In the past, hawks were equipped only with jesses and a specially resonant bell, which could be heard several hundred metres away. Hawks today are flown with tiny radio transmitters, so that they can be found more easily when they fly out of sight. For a longwing a hood is also important, to prevent the bird seeing prey before the falconer is ready to release it. Once the bird has made a kill, it may then be picked up, or 'called down' to fist or lure for food.

The key to success in all stages of training is the feeding regime. A hawk is trained when it is most receptive — such as when it is keen for its daily meal. It must not be kept short of food, however, or it will lack stamina for long flights and its health could suffer.

WINGS OVER THE DINOSAUR WORLD

Right: *Over a thousand pterosaur specimens have been found to date. This example, discovered over 200 years ago in Bavaria, remains one of the finest and most complete.*

I hold in my fingers the impression of a small, delicate skeleton, its neck arched, wings and legs jumbled together and jaws agape, just as it came to rest on the sea floor 150 million years ago. This is all that remains of a pterosaur (often referred to as a pterodactyl) — arguably one of the most extraordinary creatures ever to have existed. The animal now trapped in this extremely rare fossil once swooped over a world filled with reptiles. On land, herds of plant-eating dinosaurs such as stegosaurs were trailed by flesh-eaters such as the fleet-footed dromaeosaurs; the seas were hunting grounds for ichthyosaurs (dolphin-like fish catchers) and the huge predatory plesiosaurs. Over them all flew pterosaurs, the first true vertebrate fliers.

Following a massive meteorite impact, a radical change in the climate or some other cataclysmic event, the pterosaurs, dinosaurs and other groups died out about 65 million years ago. So all that we know about pterosaurs has been deduced from their fossil remains. Usually only the hardest tissues, such as bone, are preserved. But the shape and relative size of fossil bones reveal a great deal about basic pterosaur anatomy: they tell us how the joints worked and suggest the muscles which controlled them. Internal casts of the braincase and, on very rare occasions, the almost miraculous preservation of soft tissues, have also provided valuable insights into the nature of the brain, wing structure and body covering. The age and geographic distribution of finds, kinds of sediment in which the remains are preserved, even the 'death-pose' of the skeleton are all further grist to the palaeontologist's mill.

The first and one of the best pterosaur specimens came to light in Bavaria in 1784, but it was many years before the true identity of the fossil — a flying reptile — was agreed upon. In the intervening 200 years, many theories have evolved to describe the biology of pterosaurs, and most have been cast aside in the wake of new discoveries. Until recently, pterosaurs were regarded as an early but inevitably doomed attempt at flight. Cold-blooded and scaly, probably capable of little more than gliding, these animals were seen as a feeble prelude to birds. But these old ideas have now been swept away by new finds.

The first clue came from new studies of the pterosaur's flight apparatus. This is well preserved in remains of *Dimorphodon*. The shape of the sternum and the various

Far right: *No longer thought of as unsuccessful, gliding prototypes of birds, pterosaurs have been reinstated to their rightful place — commanding the skies of the prehistoric world.*

bumps on the upper arm showed that pterosaurs had large, powerful flight muscles. The shoulder joint was quite complex, and, as in birds and bats, enabled the wing to be swept back and forth as well as flapped up and down. The detailed preservation of a 100-million-year-old piece of wing membrane from Brazil also showed that the wing was not just a sheet stretched between the fore- and hind limbs, but a complex, layered structure containing muscles which enabled it to control its shape.

The idea of gliding pterosaurs was beginning to seem unlikely, but, if they were true fliers, how did they power their wings? Birds and bats have a 'warm-blooded' metabolism capable of sustained flight, but pterosaurs, with a 'cold-blooded' reptilian

Below: Even a half-size reconstruction of Quetzalcoatlus gives an awe-inspiring impression of how this winged giant must have dominated the air.

metabolism, would have been exhausted after a few minutes. Perhaps pterosaurs had, during the evolution of flight, also become warm-blooded. In the 1960s, a dramatic discovery was made in the Karatau mountains of Kazakhstan in Central Asia. Exquisitely preserved fossils revealed not only details of the wing's shape and extent, but the presence of numerous fine, short fibres. At last, scientists had found evidence of pterosaur fur and a potentially warm-blooded, high-performance physiology.

Tiny, pit-like openings in the limb bones are further evidence for the warm-blooded theory. As in birds, these openings helped to lighten the skeleton and improve respiration. Once airborne, fliers face the risk of overheating because the activity of the

flight muscles generates so much heat. Pterosaurs evolved a neat solution to this problem. Just beneath the outer skin the wing membranes contained a layer laced with vessels through which hot blood circulated, dispersing excess heat.

In addition to physiological demands, flight also requires a sophisticated brain. Casts of pterosaur braincases show that, unlike that of other reptiles, the brain was relatively large, complex and very bird-like, with well-developed regions concerned with coordination, balance and vision. Such brains suggest complex behaviour patterns, an idea supported by new interpretations of a common but enigmatic feature of many pterosaurs: skull crests. Crests often rise up from the back of the skull, or run along its top surface, and in some recent discoveries large, blade-like crests adorn the tips of the jaws. These distinctive structures were once believed to have had a mechanical function, such as steering. But new studies reveal that for particular species they are present on the skulls of some individuals, but not others. This suggests a quite different purpose: a display device for intimidating rivals or to attract a mate in a courtship ritual.

We now know that pterosaurs, far from being prehistoric flops, were finely tuned to the environment in which they lived. Details of their evolutionary history show this group to have been very successful, not least in the great length of time for which they existed. This group survived for over 140 million years, at least twice the length of time for which bats have existed, and similar to the current age of birds, which first appeared around 150 million years ago.

Pterosaurs also evolved into myriad different forms, as shown by the remarkable variation in how they fed. Many species independently evolved a fish grab — a fan of large teeth in the jaw tips which served to pluck fish from the surface of the water. In one case, the lower jaw developed a

long, prow-like extension, exactly as in the modern skimmer bird, which would have ploughed the water surface in the hunt for small fish. Other pterosaurs adopted a flamingo-like lifestyle, using hundreds of long, fine teeth to filter food from scoops full of water. One group had deep, wide jaws fringed with bristles. These 'flying mouths' would have engulfed insect prey on the wing, as swallows and swifts do today. Until recently all pterosaurs were thought to eat flesh, but in the last year a plant-eating form has been found. With its short, deep, toothless jaws, the skull of this animal looks oddly parrot-like and it is believed to have fed on fruit and seeds.

Most pterosaurs were only starling- to crow-sized, but some became much larger. *Pteranodon,* an ocean-going fish-catcher, typically attained wingspans of 3–5m, though specimens have been found with wingspans up to 9m — larger than any bird, living or extinct. These pterosaurs were thought to represent the maximum possible size for a flying animal, until a geologist working in Big Bend National Park in Texas stumbled across the fossil remains of

Above: *The details obtained from fossil finds build a picture complete enough to allow reconstructions such as this, of a Pteranodon. A test flight can measure the aerodynamic efficiency of pterosaur physiology.*

Right: Pterodaustro *was a filter feeder. It had hundreds of flexible, bristle-like teeth on its lower jaw, through which it could sieve tiny aquatic creatures from the water.*

Right: Gallodactylus *had a crest at the back of its skull, possibly used in a mating display. Sharp teeth confined to the front of the jaws would have gripped fish.*

Right: Ornithocheirus *had an unusual crest on both its upper and lower jaws. These prominent display devices could be used to threaten as well as attract.*

Right: Dsungaripterus *had pointed jaws with toothless tips. It may have used them as pincers to grab heavy scaled fish, cracking them open on bony knobs back in the jaw.*

Right: Dimorphodon *had large front teeth on both jaws with which it snatched up prey. These were followed on each side by 30 to 40 tiny, pointed teeth, which were used to manipulate the catch.*

Quetzalcoatlus. This animal had a 12m wingspan — the size of a small plane. Other specimens showed this animal to have long, toothless jaws and a long neck. It was originally thought that these were adaptations for scavenging the bodies of dead dinosaurs. Another look at the way the neck vertebrae fit together suggests that *Quetzalcoatlus* may have been the ultimate aerial fisher, using its huge wings to soar gently over shallow lakes, then reaching down with its rod-like neck to snap up fish in slender, spear-shaped jaws.

In a joint project with palaeontologists, aeronautical engineers attempted to recreate the largest flier of all time. Eventually they had to settle for producing a half-sized

reconstruction and, after a great deal of work, they made a model that flew and even flapped its wings. Sadly, it crashed during its first public demonstration, but not before more than 20 successful tests, many of them captured on film.

Pterosaurs and other long extinct groups may appear to have little relevance to the modern world, preoccupied as it is with problems of global climatic change and threats to biodiversity. Yet the study of such groups forms an integral part of current research programmes aimed at understanding past crises in the earth's natural history. In turn, these studies provide insights into the mechanisms which may underlie the current environmental crisis.

And beyond the utilitarian, fossils are the key to understanding the immense history of life which resulted in the living world which we inhabit today. Great adventures lie ahead, not only for those exploring the cosmos and the heart of the atom, but also for those exploring the extraordinary life of past worlds buried beneath our feet.

David Unwin

Left: Recent excavations in Brazil yielded a piece of pterosaur wing membrane, miraculously preserved for 100 million years.

PTEROSAUR ANATOMY

Pterosaurs had a bird-like skull with large eyes and long, toothed jaws. The body was short and compact. The fore-limbs carried the wings, the outer halves of which were supported by the elongated fourth finger. This gives us the name pterodactyl, from the Greek pteros, 'wing' and dactylos, 'finger'. Early forms had a long tail with a vertical flap, but they lost this as they evolved.

How much pterosaurs were able to move on the ground has been fiercely debated. Some argue that pterosaurs tucked their hind limbs up under the body and ran around like birds. But recent studies suggest that the legs sprawled out sideways and were mainly used to control the wing membranes. On the ground, pterosaurs probably stood on four limbs and moved slowly and clumsily.

CLAWING BACK THE LOST GROUND

As recently as 1980, hunters with packs of hounds were legally permitted to hunt and kill otters in their riverside strongholds. For centuries this 'sport' had been part of rural life in many areas. Although otters have never been systematically taken for their fur in Britain, bounties paid for dead otters can be traced back through the parish records in some counties. Indeed, for a long time otter population trends were estimated upon the basis of kill records published in hunters' yearbooks.

Alarm bells first sounded about 30 years ago, when hunting returns from southern England showed a sharp decline in the otter population. This decline is believed to have resulted from the widespread agricultural use of the insecticide dieldrin. Although dieldrin was withdrawn from widespread use during the 1960s and 1970s, the persistent long-term effects of chemicals may still be affecting the animal's breeding rate.

Today, the otter remains widespread in Scotland and most of Wales. It has recently gained a little ground in western and south-west England but is absent from central regions and most of the east of the country.

In 1978 a law was passed making it illegal to catch or kill an otter or attempt to do so anywhere within England and Wales. The passing of the Wildlife and Countryside Act in 1981 clarified this existing law, and extended otter protection to Scotland. The new act also made it an offence to disturb or destroy the dens of protected animals.

In recent years pollution, habitat destruction and increasing human activities, such as eel and lobster trapping, have all been blamed for the otter's decline.

The increasing use of polychlorinated biphenols (PCBs) may have also affected the reproductive success of the otter. Found in a wide range of industrial products, and released into the atmosphere when plastic is burned, PCBs contain many toxic impurities. They seep into water via landfill sites and dissolve into animal tissues, where they pass along the food chain before concentrating in the otter's fatty tissues.

Above: Encouraging the otter to recolonize areas has not proved easy. Surveys of East Anglian rivers in 1980 revealed that only three rivers showed signs of multiple habitation by otters. Two of these had lost their otters by the mid-1980s and the animals had probably vanished from the third by 1989.

Of eight otters found dead in East Anglia during the 1980s, five had levels of PCBs within their body tissues which exceeded 50 milligrams per kilogram of body tissue. Reproductive success in the otter's relative, the mink, is known to decline markedly when PCBs reach this level. One of the otter casualties, an 11-week-old cub, was found to have accumulated 62mg/kg of PCBs in its liver fat during its brief life.

Although the otter is generally a shy and retiring animal it will tolerate some degree of human activity nearby. Otter spraints (droppings) have been found along water courses in the cities of Glasgow and Cork. But the otter does need 'bolt holes' to enable it to rest and to avoid disturbance. Its favourite sites are large, overhanging trees with plenty of roots by the water's edge, but it will make do with bankside

bramble patches or old stone walls. In tree-less areas of western Scotland and Ireland, otters use natural hollows in peat bogs for shelter and for rearing young. The increasing popularity of water sports together with urban expansion, particularly in the southeast, have not improved the otter's habitat, and it is also feared that the recent privatization of the water authorities may worsen the situation.

Little can be done to help the otter until we know more about its lifestyle and needs. Conservation workers look for spraints or footprints along stretches of river bank for up to 600m at intervals of 5–8km. The amount and age of the spraints reveal information about the status of the local otter population. Male otters radio-tracked in Scotland have been shown to make use of over 40km of waterway, and this distance may be greater if the male is seeking a mate.

In East Anglia, a re-introduction scheme, initiated by the Otter Trust in 1983, aims to link isolated pockets of otters within the region. Stretches of river are assessed for their suitability, taking into account factors such as fish stocks, the availability of bank-side cover, cleanliness of the water and the likelihood of disturbance.

By the end of 1990 26 otters had been released at six sites in East Anglia, Dorset and Wiltshire. Since the scheme started, released animals or their offspring have successfully reared at least 23 litters in the wild. But the validity of re-introduction schemes has been criticized, with some people arguing that there is little point in re-introducing a species if the underlying causes for its decline have not been tackled.

Although we know more about the otter, and have improved watercourse management, the causes of the otter's decline may yet be operating. Little is still known about habitat requirements for breeding, although it seems unlikely that the heavily managed East Anglian waterways are ideal.

The size of a released population is also important, and care must be taken to ensure that inbreeding does not occur. At least 50 animals are needed to avoid inbreeding in a captive breeding programme, whereas in the wild a minimum population size of 500 is thought necessary. The schemes most likely to be successful are those involving the release of large numbers of wild-caught (rather than captive-bred) animals into high-quality habitat at a release site that is comfortably inside the species' range.

Current re-introduction programmes may not succeed in sites where the population is already low and fragmented, but one ray of hope for these areas is the ability of the wild population to recolonize previously occupied areas. Since the banning of dieldrin there has been a partial recovery in otter populations in Wales and the southwest of

Left: *The otter is a rare sight in southern and eastern Britain, where few rivers provide it with the habitat it needs.*

England through natural recolonization. Otters will travel long distances in search of a mate. Ideally, proposed reserves should be linked by corridors of suitable habitat, such as rivers and ditches, which allow the otters to move about freely and so help prevent inbreeding. Only by such means can we hope to help this beautiful mammal claw back some of its lost ground.

Tony Stones

Below: *Perhaps the best method of ensuring a healthy otter population is to provide a long, clean stretch of riverine habitat where the animals can be free of disturbance.*

LIVING THE HIGH LIFE

One of the last scientific frontiers lies not light years away in space or deep beneath the world's oceans but about 45m above the ground. This is where the trees of lowland rainforest spread their branches to reach the sun, forming a vast green roof or canopy.

Until 10 years ago, the canopy was quite literally out of reach. Biologists who tried to clamber up the vast, smooth tree trunks were met by armies of stinging, biting insects, poisonous snakes and other animals. Then, using newly developed lightweight materials, they began to build ladders and towers to get to the branches, slinging rope bridges and trapezes from one tree across to the next. Some scientists even descended on the forest canopy from above, suspended in gondolas from massive industrial cranes.

What is emerging from these explorations is the importance of this unique environment: it is now thought to contain more than half of all life, and a single rainforest tree may harbour more than 10,000 species. In the 1970s, American biologists believed there were around 10 million insect species in the world; estimates now stand at around 50 million. Yet even as these discoveries come to light, their existence is being threatened. We have destroyed half the world's tropical rainforests in the last 50 years and, according to the World Wide Fund for Nature, an area the size of Britain is still being cleared every year. Nine-tenths of Central American rain forest has already been cleared, while in Madagascar and Paraguay the rainforest will be gone in 20 years unless the rate of felling is controlled.

'Rainforest' is a fairly broad term used to describe many different kinds of forest. The popular image of tall, evergreen trees and dense humidity is that of lowland tropical rainforest. Montane rainforest, sometimes called cloud forest, has a lower canopy and is cooler and drier. Coastal mangrove forest is also a type of rainforest. Farther from the equator, in areas of lower rainfall, grows semi-deciduous tropical forest.

Seen from the air, lowland rainforest appears as a solid mass of leaves, but actually it is made up of many layers that blend into one another. Uppermost is the dry, hot, sunny realm of the tree tops, their crowns spreading out but not quite touching one another. Their average height is about 45m but giant 'emergent' trees grow to heights of 60m or more. Beneath the canopy roof, branches are festooned with climbing plants and epiphytes. Under them is a further storey; a network of smaller trees, fighting for sunlight in the humid gloom of the inner forest.

Each habitat offers a micro-environment to suit different species. Sunshine and food are available all year round in equatorial forests, so neither plants nor animals need to be as adaptable to change as those in temperate lands. In fact, specialization is the best option. Over thousands of years, rain-

avoids competition with either of its relatives by exploiting the various food sources to be found among the lower branches, between the two extremes.

The earth-shattering roar of the howler monkey is no idle display. Different troops of these social monkeys rove through the canopy calling to warn of their current position. In this way they can exploit the forest's foliage and fruit while avoiding skirmishes between competing troops.

Canopy-dwelling animals have evolved remarkable physical adaptations for their high-rise life, and for those at the very top, flight is the best method of movement. We naturally think of flying insects, birds and bats, but there are also 'flying' squirrels, frogs, lizards and even snakes. None of these can really fly, but they have adaptations for leaping or gliding between trees. The golden flying snake has specialized ribs to enable it to flatten its body and 'swim' through the air for up to 3m. The flying dragon has wings supported by rib extensions: it can glide across distances of 17m.

The colugos of Southeast Asia are the best aviators of all and can glide for up to 100m. They have a membrane stretching from the chin to the tip of the tail which encompasses all four limbs, giving these

Above: *This philo-dendron has aerial roots which it attaches to trees. Trees are the best routes to light in the dim forest, and the plant grows up the tree trunk to reach the sun.*

Right: *Birds such as the green-winged macaw plunder the forest for fruit and berries.*

forest-dwellers have adapted to their particular environmental niche, so that many have formed relationships with other, often totally dissimilar species.

The challenges of life in different layers of the canopy are met in a variety of ways by different species. To avoid conflict over territory or food sources, for example, they may keep to a particular storey, or stake their claim over an area by calling loudly. Among the opossums of South America, which all feed on invertebrates, the woolly opossums live high in the trees while grey and southern opossums keep mainly to the forest floor. The common mouse opossum

cat-sized mammals the appearance of an animated kite.

Flying is difficult in the lower canopy; birds, bats and insects all use regular flight paths to avoid branches. Some spiders spin their web across these well-used routes to catch flies and butterflies.

For larger animals, leaping and climbing are better options. Leaping animals are typically light, small and agile. Lemurs and monkeys have grasping hands and the monkeys of South and Central America have the additional advantage of a prehensile tail: the sakis of Colombia can cross distances of up to 30m in a single leap.

Heavy mammals such as orang-utans tend to stay among the lower, stronger branches. The orang does not leap across gaps, but instead sways its tree until it comes within grabbing range of the next bough, when it transfers its weight and allows the first tree to spring back. The tarsier leaps like a tree frog between creepers and tree trunks, kicking off using its powerful hind legs.

The slow loris is a small relative of the bush baby, and has developed its particular method of movement for stealth rather than speed. As its name suggests, it moves astonishingly slowly and carefully, as if in a slow-motion film, to catch resting insects and birds off-guard. The blood vessels in its limbs are exceptionally good and the slow loris can remain motionless for hours without developing muscle cramp.

The three-toed sloth's leafy diet is low in nutrients, so it moves as little as possible in order to conserve energy. Its locking claws enable it to hang effortlessly from the branches, where its coat of algae-encrusted hairs hides it from predators.

Plants, too, have adapted to life in the canopy: the most important of these are epiphytes, sometimes known as air-plants. Their seeds settle in nooks on branches and trunks high above the ground wherever there are a few grains of leaf mould or dust to support them. There are thought to be around 28,000 species of epiphyte worldwide, including many mosses, liverworts, ferns, lichens, orchids, bromeliads and even some cacti.

Epiphytes take all their food from the sun, the rain, and the debris that settles around them. Decaying leaves, animal droppings and dead insects all accumulate and are tapped for food, and many epiphytes even have water reservoirs in the base of their leaves. Gradually, an epiphyte mat builds up on the topside of tree limbs. Branches used as highways by forest animals can be distinguished because constant trampling keeps them clear of all but the smallest plants.

There are advantages and disadvantages

Left: *The flower mantis uses its resemblance to a plant to lure insect prey close — then it strikes out for the kill.*

Below: *The three-toed sloth is in no hurry for its leafy meal. It expends as little energy as possible in all its movements.*

Above: *Long-term observation projects are hurrying to gain knowledge before forests are felled for timber and entire species are lost.*

for host and guest alike. The tree loses some sunlight and gains the weight of the epiphytes, but many trees have evolved aerial roots which can take food and water from the nutrient-rich mat. For the guest plants there is the benefit of a short-cut to the sun, set against the risk of death if the overloaded branch breaks or the tree falls.

Bromeliads are epiphytes whose strap-like leaves resemble those of a giant pine-apple; in fact, they are members of the same plant family. Each one is also a minute habitat, and their water reservoirs are useful for many animals in the hot canopy. These tiny ponds attract tree frogs, salamanders and spiders, as well as the many kinds of insects which lay their eggs in the water of the ready-made nurseries.

Other arboreal plants literally keep one foot on the ground. Liana vines root in the ground but take hold on nearby trees on a light-seeking climb to the canopy, extending tendrils for support. Strangling figs work the opposite way: their seeds are scattered through the canopy in the droppings of birds and monkeys. When a seed germinates, it sends a root down to the ground. The fig then puts out leaves and further roots which eventually throttle the host tree.

Some trees escape from the clutches of climbers. The *Cecropia* employs Azteca ants as guardians. The ants live in the tree's hollow branches and feed on nectar from its leaves, protecting the tree by cutting away young epiphytes and creeper tendrils. Epiphytes receive a warmer welcome from other ant species: one Asian species has a symbiotic relationship with its ant tenants, which shelter in its hollow root chambers. The plant secretes nectar which the ants eat, in turn defending their host from animals and other plants.

Despite their name leaf-cutter ants, found only in the Americas, do not eat leaves. Individuals cut pieces of leaf from plants and trees and take them back to the nest. There, they chew them to a pulp into which they sow fungus spores. The leaf pulp provides a compost bed for the growing fungus, which the ants harvest and eat.

In many habitats the wind is an important carrier of pollen and seeds, but it hardly penetrates the dense rainforest. Instead, plants bribe flying insects, birds and bats with nectar and fruit to get their flowers pollinated and their seeds spread over a wide area. Flowers often fit one particular species of insect, increasing the chance of it carrying pollen from one bloom to another. Not all insects eat nectar; many are predators. One such, the flower mantis, looks just like a flower itself and uses its disguise to catch other insects as they land on its 'petals'.

REACHING THE TOP

Getting into the rainforest canopy has been the goal of naturalists for generations, but until recently it was less attainable than Everest. The first serious attempts to reach it were made in the 1920s by a team from Oxford University on an expedition to Guyana. It met with very limited success.

Different approaches during the 1960s and 70s involved the use of platforms, towers and bridges but all were too cumbersome to be of much use.

In 1978, Stephen Sutton, a tropical ecologist, and Andrew Mitchell (above right), a zoologist, designed a lightweight aerial walkway. In Panama, Andrew reached the canopy 30m above the ground.

Since 1987 in French Guiana, Francis Hallé and his colleagues have been using a remarkable sky-raft, measuring 600sq m in area. Using ropes and harnesses, scientists can climb up to it from the forest floor below.

Adaptation and interdependence allow survival in the stable environment of the rainforest, but the whole arrangement is extremely fragile. If one species is wiped out, its dependents die too: there are, for example, at least 80 species of fig in Amazonia, each pollinated by its own species of wasp. Localized populations are vulnerable to extinction, and even limited felling may destroy the delicate balance.

For the energetic breed of biologists now exploring the canopies of rainforests, it is a race against time to find and record even a fraction of what lives there, to understand just a little more of the world to which we belong, before any more decks of this wonderful house of cards collapse.

Sarah Foster

Left: *Dr Jellison, an Australian researcher, uses special optical equipment that makes it easier to examine smaller specimens.*

Overleaf: *The endearing orang-utan is less nimble than many canopy inhabitants. It stays among the lower branches, which are sturdy enough to bear its weight.*

ENVIRONMENTAL ISSUES

Most people, when they think of the environment, focus on the world's endangered animals and habitats. While these are undeniably vital issues in the struggle to save the planet, the most challenging question may be how humans can fit into an environmentally secure world.

With this consideration in mind, this section considers the results of the Earth Summit in Rio de Janeiro. It then looks at the way we deplete the oceans' resources when we fish for food, and examines the damaging effects on wildlife of Britain's current drought — another crisis caused in part at least by human activity.

There then follows a survey of the world's forgotten conservationists — the indigenous peoples who have plenty to teach us about living in harmony with our environment. Closer to home, we can learn about the nature reserve that potentially exists in our own garden. Wildlife-friendly tourism is explored, and we end in the remote Galapagos Islands, where tourism is managed in the best interests of the unique wildlife living there.

Left: Global changes in climate may heighten the effects of desertification in areas such as Mali in West Africa, making life impossible to sustain.

Below left: Indigenous peoples such as the Inuit have traditional lifestyles which enable them to live from the land without depleting natural resources.

Below: The rainforests are not just convenient 'clearing stations' for the greenhouse gases emitted by the developed world. They are an essential habitat for the humans and wildlife that live in them.

THE ROAD FROM RIO

UNITED NATIONS CONFERENCE ON ENVIRONMENT AND DEVELOPMENT
Rio de Janeiro 3–14 June 1992

Above: *It remains to be seen whether the world's nations can exercise the political will to fulfil the ideals of the Rio Conference.*

Right: *Nestling at dusk between the hills and the sea, Rio glows with beauty, but on the crowded streets poverty is rarely out of sight.*

The Rio Conference may turn out to be a turning point in human history, and in our relationship with the 30 million or so other species with which we share the planet. Or it could be a brief interruption on the road to the destruction of the earth's wild areas and ultimately, of ourselves.

The Earth Summit, held by the United Nations (UN) in Rio de Janeiro in June 1992, was the largest ever gathering of heads of state and governments, all in attendance to discuss the economic development and environmental protection of the planet. The Summit's organizers hoped that world leaders would respond to the central message that protecting nature is essential to economic progress.

The Summit brief covered almost every aspect of human activity, and its fundamental themes included biodiversity, climate change, forests, desertification, and sustainable development.

The planet is losing plant and animal species, and the lands they inhabit, at an unprecedented rate. At the Summit, more than 150 nations signed a Biodiversity Convention aimed at finding ways to protect species and habitats. Its particular aims are to protect forests from clearance, forestall drainage of wetlands and halt the ploughing up and fencing of grasslands.

Air pollution from burning coal and oil threatens to alter global climates through the so-called greenhouse effect. By melting icecaps and so causing rises in sea level, it could also drown low-lying areas and islands. These processes will threaten wildlife and humans. In Rio, more than 150 countries signed the Climate Convention,

Right: *Where forests are cleared for wheat and other crops in western Australia, the land is prone to erosion. It is estimated that, for every kilo of bread produced in Australia, seven kilos of topsoil are lost forever.*

Far right: *Despite their massive populations, developing countries use only a fraction of the energy consumed by the industrialized nations.*

Right: *The Amazon Pilot Project, proposed at the Summit, will help conserve habitat for the rare bearded saki.*

agreeing to the development of national strategies which prevent further increases in emissions of the greenhouse gases.

All nations agreed a Statement of Forest Principles. This is a weaker document than the Forest Convention which countries such as Britain had wanted, but it still commits countries to trying to save their forests. This applies as much to the USA and Britain, with their few surviving ancient woodlands, as to countries with vast rainforests.

The world's deserts are growing through a mixture of drought and overuse of fragile soils in dry lands. Some of the world's poorest people live in these arid areas, such as the Sahel region on the edge of the Sahara Desert, depending on the poor soil to grow food or graze livestock. The Summit agreed that a Desertification Convention should be drawn up in the following two years to lead a worldwide fight against this menace.

Western governments made commitments to ensure that their loans to Third World countries would take more notice of the environmental impact of projects such as large dams and power stations, or irrigation schemes and forestry. Environmentally damaging projects are often not economically sustainable. Dams may silt up, forests run out of trees to cut, and irrigation channels clog with weeds and salt.

Despite these initiatives, by many yardsticks the Summit was a failure. Maurice Strong, the Canadian oil millionaire turned environmental impresario who organized the Summit, said beforehand that an extra $10 billion in 'green aid' to the Third World was necessary to set the world on a path to 'sustainable development'. The entire package of measures discussed in Rio might cost $600 billion a year to implement, with a fifth of that coming in aid. But by the end of the Summit, Strong estimated that only an extra $6 billion a year had been raised, and less than $2 billion of that was certain.

Money was was not the only shortfall. The global policing of rainforests, intended under the Statement of Forest Principles, was seriously flawed. Roughly half the world's species of plants, insects and animals may live in rainforests. But Third World nations, notably Malaysia and India, were angered by George Bush's statement before the Summit that he wanted to preserve forests partly to soak up some of the gases emitted by cars and power stations in the rich nations. One Malaysian delegate told British journalists: 'If you want control of our forests, then we think there should be international control of North Sea oil, the source of much of your pollution.'

Oil figured in other thoughts, too. The great clouds of black smoke from burning Kuwaiti oil fields and the slicks that suffocated fish and killed coral in the Persian Gulf were grim reminders of how the environment could be used as a weapon of war. Strong opened the Earth Summit by saying: 'War... is a major source of environmental damage, which must be subject to greater accountability and control. This should include much stronger legal instruments... which provide effective deterrence against future environmental aggressors.'

But many nations, including the USA, opposed this idea and it disappeared without trace from the final agreements.

There were other gaps. The Third World did not want to talk about overpopulation, which is forcing humans to take over wild lands. Rich countries would not discuss 'over-consumption' and how they might use less of the world's resources. But despite the failures, there were some signs of how the world could improve after Rio.

One of the biggest beneficiaries from the Summit was the host, Brazil. It will get most of the $150 million George Bush committed before the Summit opened as the first phase in doubling US aid for the world's forests. Top of the list is the Amazon Pilot Project, which will cost rich nations $250 million in the next three years.

This project will contribute to protecting the Amazon rainforest in several ways. It will pay for the policing of national parks and new large reserves for Indian communities. It will help establish 'extractive reserves' for rubber tappers in the remote state of Acre. Here the tappers will be able to maintain the forests and harvest rubber from trees, without their land being taken over by speculators, timber companies or itinerant peasants from the east. These policies will help preserve animals such as the giant otter, one of the world's rarest otters, and the southern bearded saki, the most endangered primate in Amazonia.

The Amazon project will also pay for research into new uses for rainforest plants — from fruit flavours for Western ice creams and cosmetics for the Body Shop, to extracting chemicals from plants to treat diseases such as cancer and AIDS.

Similar work around the world will also be greatly encouraged by the Biodiversity Convention, signed by most nations in Rio. This commits countries to promoting deals where Western money pays Third World countries to make better use of their forests and other wild areas. In return, Third World countries promise foreign companies better access to their great biological wealth. There was consternation in Rio because the USA refused to sign the Convention. All the major European nations, including Britain (which wavered for several days), signed. Maurice Strong said he believed that the USA would eventually 'find a way to sign'.

Bush objected that provisions in the Convention threatened US jobs. These concerned patent rights to new products from the forests, and safety rules on new products involving biotechnology. But the head of the UN Environment Programme, Mostafa Tolba, warned that the USA could find its companies frozen out of deals with Third World countries to exploit their forests if their government did not sign.

The potential importance of such deals is summed up by the case of the rosy periwinkle from Madagascar. A chemical from this plant has provided a cure for Hodgkins Disease worth more than $100 million in sales each year. A study for the World Wide Fund for Nature stated that 'if Madagascar had received a significant part of this income, it would have been one of the country's largest sources of income'. As it is, the country gained nothing. Under the

Biodiversity Convention, future finds could give poor tropical nations large incomes. This should encourage them to preserve their forests and to let foreign companies enter them. In such ways, it is hoped that environmental protection and economic growth can go hand in hand.

However, much depends on the world's climates. There is no proof, but the man-made greenhouse effect is being blamed for everything from droughts in Africa and the Far East to the sudden arrival of tropical cyclones in previously tranquil South Pacific islands. In Indonesia, drought caused massive forest fires to rage through late 1991 and much of 1992, especially in Sumatra, home of the fewer than 500 surviving Sumatran rhinos. Much of the forests of Western Samoa in the Pacific were battered to the ground by Hurricane Val at the turn of the year. Deaths among the local population of flying foxes, which disperse seeds, may prevent the forests from recovering. In Africa, the drought that has lasted for two decades may destroy many of the continent's surviving grasslands.

These are just the first signs of potentially cataclysmic changes in climate around the

Above: *All of humankind was represented at the Summit, with each delegate bringing a unique set of needs.*

Far left: *The clear-felling of ancient forests in Washington State, USA, reveals the extent of habitat destruction even in wealthy countries.*

Left: *Rainforest plants may have endless medical applications. The beguilingly named hot-lips plant of Belize is used locally as a natural contraceptive.*

globe which, say biologists, could wipe out many of the most productive wild lands of the planet. No habitat can be considered safe, from the enormous expanses of conifer forest in northern Canada and Siberia, to the precious wetlands of Brazil's Pantanal, home of the capybara, jaguar and spectacled cayman. For such wetlands, changes in rainfall could be as damaging as global warming.

Studies commissioned by the UN for the Earth Summit confirmed that a 60 per cent cut in worldwide emissions of greenhouse gases is needed to stabilize climates. If not,

as Strong said at the start of the Summit, 'the changes in the next 60 years may be so rapid that nature will be unable to adapt and man incapable of controlling them'.

Yet the target in the Climate Convention to stabilize emissions at 1990 levels by the year 2000 is just that — a target, not a commitment. At the Summit's close, Strong called the greenhouse effect 'the most urgent crisis we face', and the failure to tackle it the Summit's most serious failure.

Some Third World nations claimed that worrying about a future climate crisis was a luxury they could not afford. Their people

Below: *Coral reefs embody the plight of nature: what takes centuries to develop can be wiped out in days by human thoughtlessness.*

had to be fed first, whatever the ecological cost. But for others it was a matter of national survival: recent studies show that the rise in sea levels as ice-caps melt in a warmed world will literally drown them.

'For some islands it may be too late,' said Robert van Lieerp, ambassador for Vanuatu which — with Tuvalu, Kiribati and the Marshall Islands — is among the tiny, flat coral Pacific islands most threatened.

The loss of such islands would be a biological as well as a human tragedy. Rising waters already threaten to outpace the growth of coral reefs, and so destroy them. Coral reefs are the marine equivalent of the tropical rainforests. They harbour a huge diversity of species. And, like forests, they have a great ability to absorb carbon from the air and surface waters, so counteracting the greenhouse effect. On land, too, the surviving forests of the Pacific islands harbour a large number of unique plant and animal species.

The Earth Summit is only the start of a process that environmentalists hope will bring some ecological sanity back to the world. 'This could be our last, best chance,' Strong said. During 1993, we should see flesh put on the bones of Rio. The Climate and Biodiversity Conventions could be up and running, with the first national plans published by Western countries to show how they will limit their emissions of greenhouse gases. Negotiations should get under way for a Desertification Treaty, and perhaps for the long-delayed Forest Convention. World production of the CFCs that destroy the ozone layer should continue to fall fast, in line with agreements made before Rio. Most important, perhaps, there should be the first meetings of the UN Commission for Sustainable Development, to be created as the first permanent watchdog of the planet's environment.

But all that is just bureaucracy. The world still awaits: the first year when more trees

Left: Recent research suggests that mangrove forests, which sustain important tropical fisheries, would not survive the fast rises in sea level that may result from global warming.

are planted than cut or burned down; the first year when less greenhouse gases are put into the atmosphere than the year before; a reduction in the number of people drinking disease-ridden water and going to bed starving; and a time when animal species are taken off the endangered list not because they are extinct, but because they are flourishing.

If the Earth Summit succeeds in its aims, then all these 'firsts' could soon be hitting the headlines.

Fred Pearce

Below: Intent mainly on sustaining exports, governments have yet to control the proliferation of cars, which are inflicting untold damage upon the environment.

FISHING FOR FOOD

More than 70 per cent of the planet is covered with water, to an average depth of 4km — making the seas the largest habitat for life on earth. Fish live in all waters, from the poles to the tropics, and have been sought for food since time immemorial. Until very recently, the sea and the food it offered were treated as an infinite resource. Today, this illusion is no longer sustainable, and we are facing the consequences of our heedless exploitation of this precious environment.

Not only do fish provide a valuable source of protein for humans, but at least 40 per cent of the world catch goes to make fish meal to feed livestock or to use as fertilizer. This is a highly inefficient use, since, by the time the fish has been processed, much of its protein content has been lost.

For most of human history, the main kind of fishing has been 'artisanal fishing' — small-scale fishing in coastal and inland waters. Although artisanal fishing today accounts for only a tenth of the world's catch of fish, in many developing countries it supplies 40–100 per cent of the animal protein in peoples' diet.

The range of techniques used for artisanal fishing is remarkable. Many are designed to trap fish moving offshore with the ebbing tide. Since prehistoric times, Fijians have used a simple semicircular wall of rocks that becomes exposed at low tide, stranding the fish. Elsewhere, in estuaries and other narrow inlets, gill nets are strung across the water. The fish cannot see these nets of fine twine and become trapped by their gill covers. Nets of different mesh sizes are used to catch various sizes of fish.

Where water currents run parallel to the shore, nets or fences are set to funnel fish into narrow-mouthed enclosures fixed to the sea bed or suspended between small boats, a process sometimes aided by shouting and splashing fishermen. Even simpler is a bundle of brushwood placed in the water to catch bottom-dwelling fish. These fish tend to seek out shelter, and so congregate in the brushwood. Lobsters have the same habit, and are trapped the world over in thorn-lined traps or baskets with a small narrow entrance, often baited with rotting fish or shellfish.

A fishing method known to all small children is the rod and baited line, a technique that can be used even in quite deep water. A more active kind of artisanal fishing is to walk through muddy shallow water, trapping fish under hand-held pots as the feet disturb them.

In clear water, sharp-eyed fishermen use spears to hunt octopus and other shallow-water species. Even more skill is needed to use a cast net — a circular net some 10m across that is thrown by hand so that it opens out just as it hits the water. Weights on its edge pull the net down, trapping shoals of fish as it sinks to the bottom.

Small fishing communities adjust their activities to the seasonal migrations of the fish, and often supplement fishing with activities such as farming for the rest of the

Above: *Traditional fishing techniques allow stocks to recover just enough to supply local communities. Whether supplies of fish can survive modern economic pressures is now seriously in doubt.*

year. Each generation hands down knowledge about the seasonal movements of fish, where they spawn and where they feed, helping to prevent overfishing.

Although such simple practices may seem to pose no threat to stocks, many small fishing communities are close to tourist developments. These not only provide new local markets, but their road, rail and air links also bring more distant markets within reach. Selling fish for cash then becomes a viable option.

Many artisanal fisheries are increasingly threatened, however, by the growth of commercial fleets, which operate just outside national waters used by local populations. Inshore, growing settlements and expanding tourism pose a range of problems. These include pollution, the blasting of reefs for building materials, and the cutting of mangrove forests for fuel and construction materials. Coral reefs in particular are extremely intolerant of pollution, since corals can survive only in clear water. Many

coastal reefs are also silted up by soil washed down from eroding inland areas.

The technology now exists to catch fish in quantities beyond the dreams of artisanal fishermen. Modern fishing vessels fall into three main categories. Factory trawlers drag weighted nets along the continental shelves to catch bottom-dwelling fish such as cod, hake and haddock, which are then transported on ice back to port.

For fish living closer to the surface, giant purse seiners are used. Their huge nets can encircle entire shoals, and the ships can carry 150 tonnes of frozen fish. Modern nets can sweep up a whole shoal in a single pass, and as stocks become smaller and more scattered, ever more sophisticated boats are built to find them. This technique suits far-ranging fish such as blue-fin tuna, marlin and sailfish.

Yellow-fin tuna, which swim deeper, are trapped by long-liners — strings of baited hooks extending up to 30km from the ship. Marlin and sailfish are also trapped on these lines. So advanced is the technology that the Japanese are developing robots to carry out this labour-intensive form of fishing.

A tragic consequence of commercial fishing is that throughout the oceans of the world millions of dolphins, turtles and other marine animals die every year, entangled in the vast nylon drift nets — some up to 50km long — which are strung out across the sea. Many of these nets break away from their vessels and drift across the oceans as vast 'walls of death' that continue to 'fish' for decades.

Another result of the increased efficiency of the fishing industry is that many stocks have been seriously over-fished. This has led to a decline in the number of whales, fur seals and sea otters. There has also been a crash in anchovy stocks off the Peruvian coast, falling catches off the Newfoundland Grand Banks, dwindling salmon runs in our rivers, and diminishing cod and herring stocks in the North Sea.

Another, less expected consequence of intensive fishing has been the decrease in average size of the fish caught. As it is chiefly the larger, mature fish which are caught, individuals that are able to breed earlier, at a smaller body size, are more likely to produce offspring. Over time, such enforced genetic selection produces smaller species. During the late nineteenth century, Atlantic cod reached weights of 90kg: today the largest reach about 11kg.

Overfishing of one species can also affect others, and today there is cause for concern at the fishing of Antarctic krill. These shrimp-like creatures are central to the southern ocean food chain, providing the staple diet of the great whales, leopard and crab-eater seals and countless seabirds. We do not know what impact the loss of vast

Above: *Puffins in the Shetland Islands recently suffered a huge slump in breeding success, probably due to overfishing of the sand eels which they feed to their young.*

Left: *Deep-sea trawlers are unselective in the fish species they catch. They can also do untold damage to the sea bed and its other wildlife.*

Right: *Aquaculture has been carried out in the Far East for thousands of years, but today, with growing populations, more and more coastal habitats are being cleared with little thought for other wildlife.*

Below: *Deep-water fish often grow slowly: the orange roughie cannot breed until it is 20 years old. Already, off New Zealand, a fishing industry barely 12 years old has reduced local orange roughie stocks by 60–70 per cent.*

numbers of krill will have on other animals.

Unfortunately, only declining catches persuade national governments to introduce limits on fishing operations, but these measures are often too little, too late. The setting of quotas has been a popular but highly questionable way of limiting catches. Fishermen wanting to extract the most revenue from their quota throw back undersized or unwanted fish. Limiting the number of days of fishing or the number of boats only leads to the development of better methods of locating and catching fish, so that more are caught on each trip.

It is estimated that up to 90 per cent of the world's fish stocks are already exploited at the maximum sustainable level. With the decline in these stocks, new sources are continually being investigated.

The farming of fish — aquaculture — is also a growth industry. It consists of keeping fish and shellfish in pens and boosting their food supply artificially. Commercial aquaculture now accounts for almost a fifth of total world fisheries production.

Milkfish are the main cultivated fish in Southeast Asia, where the rearing of fish boosts the income and food supply of small-scale farmers. Increasingly, tilapia, silver barb and common carp — all plant-eating fish — are reared in paddy fields. Farm wastes can help to boost algal growth, and the addition of pelleted food enhances the fish's diet. Tilapia are farmed in other parts of the tropics, as are trout and carp in cooler regions. Salmon are the main salt-water fish farmed in temperate regions.

With the growth of fish farming, natural habitats inevitably suffer. One third of Ecuador's mangrove forests were destroyed for prawn production between 1979 and 1983. The Philippines has lost some 60 per cent of its mangroves to aquaculture since the 1920s. Yet these habitats are vital nurseries for the fish on which many artisanal

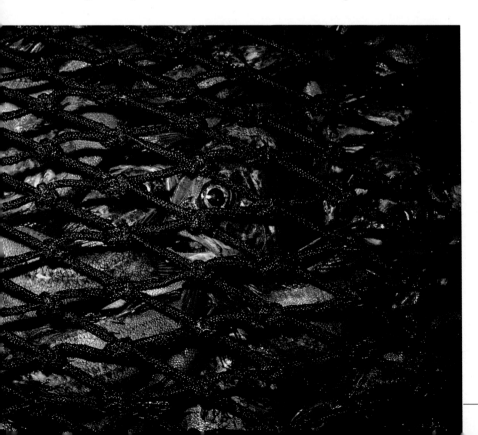

agreements. Until recently, self-regulation by countries or groups of countries such as the EC, or by specialist organisations such as the International Tuna Commission, was the rule. This system has been breaking down lately. With the decline of fish stocks that range across national boundaries, international disputes over fishing rights have become more common.

Since the 1960s a convention on the Law of the Sea has been negotiated, giving individual countries the right to set up Exclusive Economic Zones (EEZs) extending up to 332km offshore. However, the new Law of the Sea has not been ratified by enough countries to have much impact as yet.

An important recent achievement was the 1989 UN Resolution that banned all high-seas drift netting from mid-1992. Increasing international pressure for conservation of fish stocks may eventually modify the centuries-old treatment of fish as the common property of anyone capable of harvesting them.

Jill Bailey

fisheries depend. Furthermore, the culture of shrimps and prawns is often based on a supply of wild juveniles, which ultimately depletes wild stocks.

Intensive farming of fish and shellfish results in problems typical of all battery farming, such as the rapid spread of disease and of parasites, which may escape and attack wild populations. Chemicals added to control disease enter the surrounding waters, where they kill marine life. Waste food and fish excreta enrich the nearby sea, resulting in algal blooms. As an added concern, escaped fish can upset the delicate genetic balance of wild fish.

Many of these local problems are gradually being tackled by national legislation, but the worldwide decline of fish stocks has a much greater economic impact and is now being combated by international

Left: *In the shallow waters of Marlborough Sands in New Zealand, mussels are dredged from natural beds to be farmed. Young settling larvae are recruited naturally from the water, and fresh food is supplied twice-daily on the tides.*

THE GREAT DROUGHT

Above: *Drought has driven the kingfisher from many riverbanks in search of deeper water.*

Far right: *In dry weather, agriculture stretches demands on the little water there is.*

Below: *Once completely submerged, this building has been exposed by the falling water level in the Llyn Brianne reservoir.*

A drought is not a sudden event. The effects of low rainfall and long, dry periods build up over a number of seasons. Over the last five years drought conditions have afflicted parts of northern Europe, with southern and eastern England being particularly badly hit. Southeast England has lost enough rainfall since 1988 to cover the affected area to a depth of half a metre. Rivers, streams and wetlands have dried up, threatening an enormous range of wildlife.

The English drought appears to be concentrated in an area bounded by the River Humber in the northeast and the Solent on the south coast. The region to the south and east of this line has always been drier than the north and west, but the difference between the two sides of the country has widened over the five years of the drought.

In December 1991, the Intergovernmental Panel on Climate Change met in China. The panel reported that 1991 was the second warmest year, after 1990, since world records began in the middle of the last century. Of the eight warmest years in those records, seven have occurred since 1980. According to the panel's estimates, the global mean temperature will probably have increased by 1°C by the year 2030. This is less than in previous estimates, partly as a result of the global depletion of ozone, which is a heat-retaining gas.

Much of the undisputed current global warming is probably due to the huge amounts of carbon dioxide (CO_2) and other gases released into the atmosphere from road vehicles, power stations and factory chimneys. Most scientists agree, however, that a direct link has not yet been proven between human activities and global warming. The planet has seen many cycles of hot and cold in its history. The most recent major warming occurred between 1920 and 1940, and was due in part to the 'El Niño' effect. Current and wind changes in the eastern Pacific Ocean periodically cause the ocean surface to warm up by as much as 4°C above normal, resulting in climatic changes in tropical atmosphere circulations. The recent droughts in Africa are thought to be connected with El Niño phenomena.

Since 1988, the shortfall of rain in the UK has been gradually gaining ground over occasional exceptionally heavy downpours. Yet consumers have not adjusted their habits to reflect this. Domestic users consume two-thirds of the 17.3 billion litres of water used daily in England and Wales.

A significant factor in the drought in southern and eastern England is the fact that this region has a concentration of wealth as well as of population. A family of two adults and two children uses around 500 litres of water a day. This tends to be higher in wealthier areas, where washing machines, dishwashers, lawn sprinklers, hosepipes for car cleaning — and cars to be cleaned — are thicker on the ground.

Up until 1989, when the National Rivers Authority (NRA) was set up to monitor and regulate the privatized water industry, water companies were fairly free to draw as much water as they wanted from rivers, boreholes and streams. Over-extraction has reduced flows in rivers and lowered groundwater levels to a point where rain and snow are insufficient to top them up.

Natural water reserves are held in underground lakes and streams, and in porous rocks called aquifers. They maintain a level known as the water table. Many surface rivers, ponds, wells and springs depend on minimum water table levels for their own water. As the water table dips below normal levels, the rivers begin to dry up.

River headwaters have moved downstream as springs have dried, and some rivers have developed leaks as the water table beneath them has retreated. The NRA has published a list of at least 40 rivers with dangerously reduced flows.

Dried out stretches of waterway seriously affect water-dwelling wildlife. Dry conditions may be fatal to larvae of insects such as mayflies and caddis flies, and crustaceans such as crayfish and freshwater shrimps, since they are not mobile enough to move downstream as the water disappears.

Fish such as trout and salmon may be cut off from traditional spawning beds by dry stretches. Where fish of the trout and salmon family do spawn, a reduced speed of flow may kill the eggs by allowing silt deposits to smother them. Low flow rates and high summer temperatures may result in water low in oxygen: trapped in stagnant pools, fish of all species soon die. A further deadly effect results from the concentration of pollutants from agricultural chemical run-off and industrial discharges.

Where low flows have resulted in silting, channels tend to become progressively wider and shallower. This affects those fish, like trout, which prefer fast flows over beds of gravel or stone. The NRA has been introducing gravel and stone into river and stream beds in the Kennet valley in the Cotswolds, to reduce the size of the channel while increasing the water flow speed.

When summer flows in rivers and streams fall, some of the first creatures to

suffer are invertebrates, including insects, crustaceans, and molluscs such as snails and freshwater mussels. With the decline of invertebrates and plants, bird populations which feed on them also suffer.

The falling water table affects river margins and adjacent meadows. Flat riverside terrain is drying out to the point where grasses, sedges and rushes are dying off. The hardened soil along the river edge does not suit birds such as snipe, redshank and curlew, which feed by probing soft, muddy soils with their bill. Birds such as the mallard, moorhen and coot can adapt to a variety of terrains, but more specialized birds such as herons, grebes and kingfishers forsake affected rivers for deeper water.

The mammals most affected by receding waterways are otters and water voles, both of which have been declining for a period longer than the current drought. The water vole is dependent on waterside plants such as rushes and sedges for its food, and as these dry out it becomes more vulnerable.

Amphibians such as frogs, newts and toads are also affected by drought, as many of them use shallow temporary puddles for breeding and spawning. In drought conditions, puddles and pools may dry out before the eggs have had time to hatch, or tadpoles to develop fully.

Members of the European Wildlife Rehabilitation Association have pointed out that some of our best known and best loved non-aquatic wildlife species are also suffering from the drought. Foxes, badgers and hedgehogs are all being brought to clinics suffering from dehydration and food shortage. Badgers and hedgehogs depend on species such as earthworms and slugs, which are often in low supply as drought-stricken ground hardens up. Consequently, these mammals are all having to hunt farther afield, leading to an increase in deaths and injuries from traffic. Hedgehogs are increasingly being forced to forage during

Left: *The water vole's diet is highly specialized, and as sources of waterside plants literally dry up, this scarce mammal is further endangered.*

the day rather than at night. This renders them vulnerable to fly and maggot infestation, against which they have no protection.

The extent to which we are all implicated in recent climatic changes is uncertain but what is clear is the need for us to stop treating water as an inexhaustible resource. By recognizing the effects of drought conditions on wildlife, we may also be able to prevent animals and plants from suffering further ill-effects.

Duncan Brewer

Below: *Rosebay willowherb is a dry-terrain plant which has flourished as river margins and adjacent meadows have dried out.*

PEOPLE UNDER PRESSURE

*Right: **In Papua New Guinea, the government has set up 'safe havens' where tribes can live free from further interference.***

*Below: **The San bushmen of Botswana and Namibia survive by using an extensive knowledge of their desert home to exploit its sparse resources. Here, they take ostrich eggs from a nest.***

Amid the disparate interests clamouring for their part in preserving the bio-sphere, there is a group for whom conser-vation is a life and death matter — the indigenous peoples who inhabit the forests, deserts, and other shrinking wild regions at the centre of conservation concerns. These people, living lives virtually unchanged for thousands of years, have frequently been ignored in the scramble to save the planet. Governments and businesses have often seen them as an impediment to develop-ment, and those wanting to exploit the land have made deliberate attempts to move indigenous peoples out of their traditional territories. This has led to their confinement in reservations and camps a fraction of the size of their tribal lands. Those people unwilling to move have been persecuted and even killed.

Indigenous peoples are as much a part of the modern world as those trying to help or exploit them, and it is their right to participate in any decisions about the con-servation of their traditional territories. Conservationists have been almost as guilty as commercially interested parties in ignor-ing the wishes of the indigenous peoples themselves. There has been a tendency to romanticize them, seeing them as 'noble savages', living lives of perfect innocence. This can lead to the worst sort of tourism, in which, as the tourist bus approaches, the tribal villagers shed their Western jeans and shirts, don a few ethnic accessories, and carry out 'traditional' dances and rituals in return for a hand-out from the visitors.

Almost too late, many conservationists are realizing that indigenous peoples have

an enormous amount to teach the rest of the world about the last wildernesses. Their knowledge and skills are encyclopaedic, and their age-old lifestyles are often sustainable in a way that puts the consumer societies of the developed world to shame. Without the participation of indigenous peoples, little progress is likely in the urgent struggle to conserve the planet's riches.

Many of the world's farmer-herders have developed cycles of seasonal activity which go back thousands of years, following patterns of food-gathering which do not exhaust the land. The Tuareg nomadic farmer-herders of the Aïr Mountains in Niger graze their sheep, goats and camels in wooded mountain valleys in the hot, dry season of the year. When the rainy season approaches, they move the herds down to the surrounding plains. Half of the Tuareg

population live in permanent villages. These people depend on small garden plots, and on barter of produce for essentials which they do not produce themselves, such as salt, cereals and dates.

In many cases, indigenous peoples are able to live sustainable lifestyles partly because there is so much land to support each individual. The Yanomami people of Brazil, for example, number about 9000, and occupy some 94,000sq km of rainforest. The total Indian population of modern Brazil is just 250,000, a twentieth of what it was at the time of the Spanish conquest.

The Yanomami grow much of their food on small plots in forest clearings, moving to new 'gardens' every two or three years to allow the cultivated land to revert to the forest and regenerate itself. The Yanomami move their villages every five to ten years.

While four-fifths of their food comes from the plots they cultivate, they acquire much of their dietary protein and vitamins by gathering and hunting fish and game, nuts, fruits and honey from the forest itself.

The Yanomami, like other Amazonian tribes, look upon the game they hunt, and all the creatures of the forest, as their ancestors. This reverence for the environment and for everything that lives in it is often found among indigenous peoples, and helps to ensure that game is taken carefully, and without waste. The Inuit hunter apologizes to the polar bear before killing it, addressing it respectfully as 'uncle'. The !Kung clan of San Bushmen will not hunt the elephant at all, because they consider its intelligence to be too close to their own.

This respect for the natural world often extends to the sympathetic exploitation of plants. The tribes of the Papua New Guinea highlands use over 600 species of plant, most of them gathered wild. They build their houses from grasses and thatched leaves. Traditional dress is made from bark,

Left: The Inuit rely on hunting and fishing to sustain them in the frozen reaches of their northern homeland. Traditional hunting methods include a respect for prey rare among recreational hunters in the developed world.

leaves and twines of plant fibre. In the forest the tribespeople gather plants to make dyes, medicines, cosmetics and poisons, as well as eating a bewilderingly large range of roots, fungi, leaves, fruits and nuts. Tools, ropes, baskets, musical instruments, weapons and ornaments all come from materials growing in the forest.

The Papua New Guinea highlanders have been cultivating crop plots for almost 10,000 years in fertile highland valleys. Their expert agricultural practices include the use of drained swamps and complex networks of carefully regulated drainage

Left: According to the Yanomami creation myth, the first people were transformed into the animals that inhabit the Brazilian forests today. Hunting is kept at a level that ensures the forest is never depleted of these 'ancestors'.

Right: *The dama gazelle is a rare species that has benefited from the nature reserve established in the Air Mountains of Niger. In helping the resident Tuareg people, the reserve's sponsors have ensured that rare animal species are less likely to suffer the effects of overgrazing.*

Below: *Medicinal plants are commonly exploited by indigenous peoples. This young Solomon Islander has had his broken finger splinted with a raralu leaf.*

ditches and canals. By managing their water supplies, using rich mulches of decaying vegetable matter, and allowing short fallow periods, the highland tribes maintain a horticulture that is constantly replenished.

In great contrast to the lifestyle of the highlanders, the San Bushmen of southern Africa are hunter-gatherers who have never cultivated crops or herded animals. Inhabiting desert lands where hunger, dehydration and thirst can be rapid killers, the San have one of the highest protein intakes in the world, and are masters at surviving in this harsh terrain. The San are Africa's oldest human residents, and may once have occupied the whole continent. Today they mainly inhabit parts of Botswana and Namibia which colonizers of many nationalities and races have found impossible to settle or exploit.

Highly skilled hunters, the San take over 80 species of animal, using bows and arrows, spears, snares and traps. They use a poison on their spear and arrow heads taken from the pupae of flea beetles. While the men hunt, the women and young children forage for tubers, fruits and nuts. All

may travel great distances in the course of a day, taking advantage of the availability of water, shelter and seasonal produce.

The !Kung people, one of the San tribes, live in small groups in Namibia and Botswana, moving between water holes and areas rich in food. However, very few San Bushmen still live a purely traditional life. Some of the young men go away to work for the South African Army while others have accepted the convenience of official settlement camps, with water on tap. Nearly all are influenced in some way by the outside world.

Other indigenous peoples have also reached a cross-over point between old and new styles of life. They have begun to take paid work, using money to buy food and goods sold by traders and in stores, rather than foraging daily. Conservationists should not be too quick to condemn such moves. Fresh water on tap, for example, is a huge asset to people used to the daily struggle to find water in conditions of drought.

The Australian Aborigines, the highlanders of Papua New Guinea, and, increasingly, the San Bushmen of southern Africa are all becoming ever more involved in the developed world. Political and economic pressures have been a major factor, as governments cast a longing eye on extensive tribal lands and resources. Cultural pressures also play their part, as the younger generations grow impatient with tradition and hanker after some of the aspects of the modern world brought home by contact with people outside the tribe. Despite having a foot in both worlds, these groups still retain close links with the land, its plants and its animals, and their communities are still repositories of extensive knowledge, though this, too, is under threat as the older generations die.

Like the San, the Australian Aborigines have inhabited their lands for thousands of years. Island-hopping from Southeast Asia some 50,000 years ago, the first Australians radically altered the environment which greeted them. Using fire to clear the vegetation and also as an aid to hunting, the Aborigines transformed forest regions into open savannah-like plains, ensuring the supremacy of the fire-resistant eucalyptus tree and causing the extinction of many species which depended on plants unable to survive the fire treatment.

The damage that the first Aborigines inflicted on the land has been infinitely exceeded by their descendants' suffering at the hands of European settlers. It is remarkable that these people have been able to retain some of their rich cultural traditions despite racist victimization, the usurping of

Below: *Despite hundreds of years of persecution, some of Australia's Aborigines still preserve a life of astonishing integration with their vast, harsh environment.*

Far right: *This Huli wigman from Papua New Guinea sports a wig made from the hair of family members.*

Below: *In Thailand, members of the Akha hill tribe work on a coffee and macadamia plantation. Such projects attempt to reconcile the demands of a market economy with the needs of indigenous peoples.*

important ritual lands and sites, and the institution of crudely inadequate 'reservations'. One tradition that has been undergoing a revival among some Aborigine groups is the practice of foraging for 'bush tucker', or wild foods. With reservation stores selling heavily sugared junk-food, sliced white bread and litres of sweet tomato ketchup, obesity and diabetes have become serious problems for listless reservation-dwellers. However, trials have shown a remarkable turn-around in diabetic conditions and general health when traditional bush-tucker is eaten to replace store-bought processed foods. The traditional diet is extremely varied, with a wide range of nuts, fruit, roots and tubers, as well as animal protein from many different creatures. Some items are particularly nutritious: the billy-goat plum may contain more vitamin C than any other known fruit.

The Aborigines have suffered from the exploitation of their native lands for commercial interests — to the extent that many of them are confined to reservations. But nowhere is the effect of environmental depredation more apparent than in the South American rainforests. Although the fate of the rainforests has a high media profile, the effect of their destruction on indigenous peoples is rarely discussed. As the trees are decimated so are countless insect species and everything else that thrives beneath the forest canopy, from birds, frogs and snakes to monkeys, jaguars — and the people of forest tribes. Without the forests, the forest people become extinct; they are too dependent on the forest's resources and too few in numbers to survive in the outside world. As an additional problem, diseases brought into the Amazon region by loggers, miners and farmers have wiped out entire tribes who lack immunity to them.

Properly consulted and rewarded, forest tribes could help the outside world to reap the benefits of the forests' diversity, for the forests have far more wealth to give than the short-term profit obtainable from timber. Even through simple agriculture local tribes can create foreign exchange for debt-ridden governments, while maintaining the habitats essential to their own survival. Rubber tappers have shown how to harvest wealth from constantly renewed resources. Some of the Kayapo Indians of Brazil do the same with brazil nuts, which they harvest from single, scattered trees, rather than from plantations. They sell the oil, which they process themselves, to the 'green' cosmetic industry.

The highlanders of Papua New Guinea have had similar success with the growing and marketing of organic coffee beans. Tribespeople gather the beans from trees growing in different parts of the forest. They then sell these beans, grown without the use of pesticides or fertilizers, to small

European organizations who can find a ready market for organic coffee.

In those regions where commercial coffee plantations have been established, there has often been strife between the entrepreneurs setting up the projects and the tribespeople who both own the land and work on the plantations. Because they are unaccustomed to regular hours of work, tribespeople may fail to gather coffee crops at the crucial time in their ripening cycle, spoiling the harvest. These people also feel that they receive too small a proportion of any profits in return for their labour.

This conflict shows the gulf of understanding that can exist between groups from the developed world and indigenous peoples. There is a fine line between cooperation and exploitation. We need to learn this distinction if we are to benefit from the vast human resources that exist in the few places where people still live in sympathy with their environment.

Duncan Brewer

PEOPLE OF THE AIR MOUNTAINS

The Aïr Mountains of Niger, which are home to about 5000 Tuareg subsistence farmers and herders, are also inhabited by rare populations of ostrich, addax and dama gazelle. The Aïr Mountains are of particular interest to conservationists because of their unspoilt nature and regionally rare mammal populations. The Tuareg farmers and herders survive with their vegetable plots and seasonal grazing areas, causing negligible damage to the environment. Both water supplies and vegetation are sparse, but sufficient for the small Tuareg population to survive most of the time. During periodic droughts, however, there is a damaging loss of crops and herd animals. Then the Tuareg migrate out of the region in large numbers, driven by disease and lack of food.

Formalized in 1988, *the Aïr and Ténéré National Nature Reserve is managed by the Nigerean Wildlife Service, and sponsored by international donors including the IUCN, WWF, and the Swiss and Danish governments. The reserve is over 77,000sq km in size — twice the size of Switzerland. Unlike many other nature reserves, the Aïr project concerns itself with the problems of human as well as wildlife survival in this fragile environment, rightly recognizing that without an infrastructure to protect the Tuareg inhabitants during times of drought, the wildlife will suffer from overgrazing. The project has initiated development activities including health care and well-digging, and the aim is for the Tuareg themselves to manage this huge protected area.*

WILDLIFE IN THE GARDEN

Above: *Buddleia is known as the 'butterfly bush' — with good reason, as its blooms attract clouds of peacock and other butterflies.*

The garden has always provided food and lodging for an astonishing variety of wildlife, and never more so than in these days of mechanized agriculture. Copses, hedgerows and ponds are all vanishing fast to make way for more efficient farming, and the suburban jungle can literally be a life-saver for creatures in search of habitat. However small your garden, there is always something you can do, some corner you can prepare, to help wildlife. And having followed a few simple steps, you can sit back and watch nature's changing seasons from your own doorstep.

The chill November air signals the decline of summer insects, and small mammals begin their winter retreat in secluded parts of the garden. This is the last opportunity to watch brimstone, tortoiseshell and peacock butterflies lap up their last drink of nectar from ivy flowers before they creep into dry, sheltered spots to hibernate for the winter. Starlings soar in energetic displays, crowding the sky as they gather to roost. Flocks join forces to form huge crowds that snuggle up for warmth, raising the temperature enough to ensure their survival. Keeping out the cold also becomes the winter preoccupation of tits, robins and finches, as they fluff their feathers up to create extra insulation. Watch, too, for the crest and pinkish plumage of waxwings; a flock of these fruit-lovers will strip a tree bare before moving on for their next meal.

Towards the end of the year foxes begin to court. Noisy fights between rivals ring out on still December nights, when piercing screams are a response to bites. Milder nights tempt badgers out on late foraging

Right: *The common frog is the gardener's ally, as it devours slugs, snails and insects.*

trips. Bats emerge from their moist winter retreats — caves or hollow trees — and on warmer days they may risk a daylight flight. On clear, frosty January mornings, you may also spot wild mammals such as squirrels, rabbits, and foxes searching for food — try to creep up to them downwind.

By March some birds have begun to nest. Sheds and garages provide a refuge for robins while thrushes and chaffinches hide among leafy shrubs or evergreens.

Spring is traditionally the season of birth, and there are plenty of new arrivals in the wildlife garden. By March, rabbits have produced their third litter since January. Badger cubs will soon be out on a foraging trip with their watchful mother. For hedgehogs cold spells at this time of year can prolong hibernation, however, and reduce the chance of more than one litter. By May they are circling each other excitedly for long periods as the male woos his mate. You can

help hedgehogs by sparing the slug pellets which poison them; instead, try putting down broken eggshells to ward off slugs.

Early spring is the best time to watch for birds in the garden as territorial battles begin; house sparrows and starlings jostle for a nest site in early April. The dawn chorus reaches its crescendo in May as new species announce their arrival and individuals come back into full song after each brood. Many people stop feeding birds in spring but you can continue all year. Putting out crushed nuts or moistened bread ensures that fledglings are in no danger of choking on larger morsels. Later feeding particularly benefits the greenfinch, which breeds in early summer when seeds ripen. Look out for the male's magnificent, olive-green plumage and yellow tail flashes.

Also growing up quickly are the young of grey squirrels. In woodlands they traditionally eat the fresh shoots, buds and flow-

Below: *Leave a few windfalls for the fieldfare, a regular winter visitor to our gardens.*

hibernation. She alone survives the winter, by burrowing deep into the soil beneath a tree. She revives herself by shivering to warm her body, then feeds from spring blooms such as hawthorn and sallow.

If you have a pond, clear weed from it in March to make room for frogspawn. Sit by the pond with a torch on spring nights, and you will be amazed by the number of visitors. Look out on sunny June days for the spectacular blue-and-green male emperor dragonfly zooming about the water's edge as he fiercely defends his territory.

As summer nears and the days become drier, your pond will become a cool oasis for weary birds. Hot summers present problems for swallows, house martins and song thrushes, which all use mud to build a nest. Swifts search for a roof space in which to make a home, clinging to the eaves with their weak but sharp claws. Parent birds search diligently for food in order to feed

Left: *Bumblebees are ideally shaped for the tubular blooms of lupins and foxgloves. Look for the pollen baskets on their hind limbs.*

Below: *Now common in urban areas, the grey squirrel is an inquisitive and much-loved garden resident.*

ers of trees such as oak but they will readily raid horse chestnut or hazel trees. Unlike the red squirrel the grey squirrel can live quite happily in gardens and hedgerows.

On milder, sunny days butterflies take to the wing for the first time since their winter hibernation. Buddleia, red hot pokers, hebes or michaelmas daisies in the garden will attract the attention of several species, including the tortoiseshell. The pale yellow wings of the brimstone butterfly blend perfectly with vegetation as it settles to feed from thistles, primroses and other flowers. The comma butterfly also rises early from its winter sleep to mate in March, laying its first eggs in July. The comma is easily identified by the ragged edges to its wings. From June, look also for the spiny black caterpillars of the peacock butterfly which give rise to a new generation in July.

If you have ever come across a bumblebee stumbling aimlessly about your lawn it was probably a queen emerging from

a nest full of hungry mouths. Young birds land awkwardly as they try to master flight, but resist the temptation to pick them up as this will only break down the bond between the fledgling and its parent. Prolonged dry spells prevent many birds from pecking worms from the hard soil, although ripening seeds can now be found.

In addition to the hungry birds there are plenty of other mouths to feed in the garden. Pet food or finely minced beef is a favourite with hedgehogs and is thought to be much better for them than bread and milk. The tiny young are born blind with short soft, white spines, but their dark spines protrude within a few days. If you are lucky you may see mother and young travelling nose to tail as they forage for beetles, worms and slugs. The male hedgehog plays no part in rearing the young.

Female bats are pregnant with their single young in summer. A biological clock allows them to slow down the development of their foetus when food supplies run short in cooler weather. By July young pipistrelle bats should be catching their first moths and flies, and by August females are leaving the nursery roosts to court the males.

Below: If you see a spider guarding its silken egg sac it is certainly a female.

Two groups of insect you are likely to hear but not see are the grasshoppers and bush crickets, whose whirring songs are a familiar summer sound. While grasshoppers feed entirely on plants, bush crickets include other insects in their diet.

Cascading russet leaves and lingering damp mists hail the arrival of autumn. The garden fills with the aroma of decaying leaves and rotten fruit — a feast for garden wildlife. This is the true season of gluttony. Mammals, birds and even invertebrates fatten up on ripe fruits before the winter months. Sprinkle apples and pears with a mixture of honey and water and lay them on the lawn. Before long they will draw down butterflies eager to take their last

stock of sugar before tucking themselves behind ivy for the winter.

Badger cubs, now independent, seek out worms and fungi on damp nights and look for their own living quarters. Rodents nibble on toadstools, and squirrels stockpile hazelnuts and acorns for later consumption.

Now is the time to put out offerings for the birds if you want to encourage regular winter visitors. Suspend bags of peanuts or sunflower seeds outside your favourite windows and wait for tits, greenfinches or siskins to visit. Chaffinches will prefer a store of smaller seeds. Scatter fatty food scraps on the ground for blackbirds, dunnocks and robins.

Suzanne Jones

WILDLIFE & TOURISM

Above: *As the trend for more unusual holidays continues, tourists are becoming a familiar sight to the penguins of Antarctica.*

By the end of the decade, tourism will be the world's largest industry and its potential for changing our global environment enormous. Each year, over 400 million people worldwide take international holidays, and the number is ever rising. Tourists are not only becoming more numerous, many of us are also becoming more demanding. We want more action, more adventure, and we want to go somewhere 'unspoilt', where conventional tourism has not yet stamped its indelible mark.

Responding to this demand, for the 1990s tour operators are offering a wider range of wildlife holidays than ever before. And whether it's humpback whale-watching off Newfoundland, swimming with the sea lions of the Galapagos, or experiencing the 'untamed wilderness' of Zimbabwe or Nepal, the wildlife-watching trend is growing fast. Some conservationists are heralding it as a potential force for environmental good. Certainly, it helps us to appreciate what we may lose if we continue to destroy the planet at the current pace, but we must plan now if wildlife tourism is to have a positive impact on the environment — or at least if it is to avoid the environmental abuse of traditional tourism.

Tourism must become sustainable — that is, it must not take from the environment more than can be naturally replaced, or alter a habitat beyond repair. Past evidence offers little cause for optimism, however: the impact of mass tourism on the world's most popular holiday destinations has been disastrous and, tragically, irreversible.

In the Alps, hundreds of square kilometres of forest have been cleared to make

Right: *Tourists eager for photo opportunities often disturb the very wildlife they have come to observe.*

Governors
MASAI MARA GAM
KENYA

Above: *In the central African country of Rwanda, gorilla-watching is the second largest source of foreign revenue, bringing in £300,000 a year.*

Right: *In Amboseli National Park, Kenya, each lion attracts some £15,000 every year in foreign revenue. Sadly, the tourists' four-wheel-drive vehicles destroy plant life and erode the landscape.*

endemic monk seal is one of tourism's most tragic victims. The Mediterranean monk seal used to haul out of the sea to breed on sandy beaches — just the type tourists like. Now the seals have been pushed out and their breeding rate has suffered to the extent that this species is now Europe's rarest mammal and is faced with extinction. In the Caribbean, local facilities cannot cope with the waste created by tourists. Pollution and habitat loss have resulted in rare species such as the Hawaiian monk seal, manatees and turtles being pushed to the brink of local extinction.

Ironically, it is often the wildlife which is so threatened by tourism that attracts the tourists. But a desire to see animals in their natural surroundings is no guarantee that wildlife tourism is environment-friendly. The popular Greek island resort of Zakynthos has the largest known rookery of rare loggerhead turtles (around 2000) in

way for 15,000 ski lifts and cable cars and 40,000km of ski runs. This deforestation causes floods and mud-slides in the valleys, and has taken its toll on wildlife. 49 per cent of the Alps' remaining forest is now damaged or dying as a result of the damage caused by such tourist developments.

In Venezuela, tourist agencies use the chemical dioxin to kill off unsightly seaweed on tourist beaches. As a result, millions of fish have been exterminated.

Around the Great Barrier Reef — one of Australia's greatest tourist attractions — fragile mangrove swamps are being destroyed to make room for tourist facilities. Without the mangroves, the reef itself may become choked with sediment.

Tourism has only occurred on an immense scale for the last 40 years or so, but during this short time ill-planned holiday developments have destroyed many coastal habitats. The Mediterranean has perhaps suffered the worst damage, and its

the Mediterranean. During the breeding season the females come ashore at night to bury their eggs on sandy beaches. This coincides with the main tourist season, and during the 1980s the turtles became something of a tourist attraction in their own right. Unfortunately, turtles and tourists are not a harmonious combination. Scores of sunbathers unwittingly trampled the buried eggs during the day and many went turtle-watching at night, armed with lanterns which frightened the turtles into abandoning their nesting attempts.

While turtle-watching is relatively new, the safari is a well-worn formula for a wildlife holiday, although tourists keen to watch animals in the wild can inadvertently harm the species they come to see.

But many conservationists argue that without the safari business, much of Africa's wildlife would long ago have been killed off for financial gain, or its habitat destroyed

Left: *Conservation organizations such as Earthwatch offer people the chance to encounter wildlife, like this young hyena, at close quarters.*

for agriculture. In many developing countries tourism is often the only practical argument in favour of conservation, and it certainly can be lucrative. Almost one third of Kenya's income comes from tourism and most of the tourists come for the wildlife. Some countries, notably Costa Rica, Belize, Kenya and Rwanda, have set up national parks as a direct result of tourist interest, protecting sensitive natural areas from industrial or agricultural development. This may seem encouraging, but local people often depend on the land, and for them, turning an area into a national park may simply deprive them of their living.

Two encouraging examples of schemes that respect the needs of local people can be found in opposite corners of the world. Farmers in one area of Belize have voluntarily limited slash-and-burn farming methods to create a wildlife sanctuary. Here, the black howler monkey is not only protected, but also draws foreign tourists who bring

welcome revenue for the farmers. In parts of New Guinea, instead of destroying the habitat of the local fauna by logging, local people have set up butterfly farms within the rainforest. In this way, they harvest the products of the forest — in this case butterflies — which they sell to tourists. While tourists continue to come to the region, it will be in the New Guineans' better long-term interests to preserve the forest, rather than destroy it for short-term gain.

Good planning and management can help such ventures succeed, but fragile places are ultimately threatened as more and more tourists wish to visit them. The Cairngorm Mountains in the Scottish Highlands form Britain's largest nature reserve and are one of the last untouched wild areas left in the country. But these beautiful mountains are suffering due to their very popularity. The plant life on their granite summits has been devastated by the feet of thousands of enthusiastic climbers. On the slopes, ground-nesting birds like the dotterel, ptarmigan, and golden plover are disturbed by skiers, mountain bikers, bird-watchers and plant collectors. Tourism here brings enjoyment for visitors and prosperity for local people, but sadly is at the expense of wildlife.

The story is the same the world over, but it is possible to achieve the right balance. Fewer than 450 mountain gorillas survive in the wild, 280 of them in the Virunga Volcanoes region that straddles the borders of the central African states of Uganda, Zaire and Rwanda. The latter two countries are very poor indeed, and it is a stark fact that, were it not for tourist interest, the gorillas in these countries would not be there. Gorilla-watching is very carefully controlled in Virunga: tourist groups taken into the forest are kept small — usually only half a dozen people at a time. The experience for the tourist is unforgettable and local people gain jobs as guides. But even in such a well-managed scheme, there is cause for concern. Several gorilla families have become used to humans, and they may now be easier targets for poachers. Also, such close proximity to humans may expose the gorillas to the risk of catching diseases to which they have no immunity. But in these often war-torn and poverty-stricken nations there are few practical alternatives to tourism if the gorillas are to survive.

The need for this kind of careful and sensitive management is slowly being recognized, often in order to right the wrongs that have grown out of inadequate management in the past. The Kenya Wildlife Service is trying to raise around £80 million to improve its national parks. The money will be spent on better, but fewer vehicles and roads for tourist use, and on more wardens. Tourists will enjoy value for money, locals will receive jobs and training, and the animals will be left in relative peace.

In Western Australia, the fragile ecosystem of the Bungle Bungle region has been threatened by a huge influx of tourists since 1982. But control over the number of camp sites, a policy of encouraging visitors to keep their litter with them, and close monitoring of tourist movements has ensured the least possible damage. In Britain too, carefully managed tourist schemes such as Dartmoor's Tarka project are taking off. The Tarka project is designed not only to

Above: *A well concealed hide (bottom) can enable tourists to observe wildlife without causing the unnecessary disturbance that at present is all too common (top).*

Far right: *An inquisitive polar bear begging for food may provide the ideal photo opportunity for a coachload of tourists, but such interactions raise important questions concerning the impact of people on a once remote and undisturbed wilderness.*

Below: *United Nations predictions estimate that, at the current rate of development, as much as 95 per cent of the Mediterranean coast will have been built on within the next 40 years.*

preserve the countryside, and in particular the otter, but also to help the local rural economy by encouraging tourists to stay in local bed-and-breakfasts off the beaten track. The Tarka project is such a good example because it looks at tourism management from a universal standpoint — taking into account the needs of local people, tourists and wildlife alike.

Projects such as this suggest that tourism and conservation need not be mutually exclusive. In a world with an increasingly environment-conscious public, the search for unspoilt nature will only grow and must be tackled head-on. In several parts of the world, innovative and exciting new ideas are already taking off. In Queensland, Australia, for example, plans are in progress

for the construction of rainforest walkways that would allow tourists to see the animals of the tree canopy without disturbing them. If these schemes expanded to the rainforests of the developing nations, tourism could provide a much more permanent and sustainable income than could be obtained by destroying forest for its timber or land.

Another great idea for linking tourism with conservation is that of the conservation holiday. Earthwatch is an organization set up in 1971 to use the money available from tourists to help finance environmental research projects. Volunteers pay to join a project, which may involve anything from monitoring dolphins to exploring the biodiversity of the rainforest canopy. Around 3500 people now take part in Earthwatch

projects every year, making conservation their holiday. A number of other watchdog and voluntary organizations have been set up recently to reconcile the needs of the environment with our needs as tourists. All are contributing to the gradual 'greening' of the global tourist industry.

With careful planning and management, wildlife tourism may prove to be a positive force in the environmental battle to save the planet. But it may be time for us to rethink our whole attitude to wildlife. Nothing is more enriching than encountering rare and beautiful wildlife at close quarters in its natural, unspoilt habitat, and we must preserve wild places and the species they contain for this very reason. But we must also regard wildlife as more than just something for our enjoyment, and ask ourselves if we have the right to invade every corner of the planet. If wildlife tourism is to work for conservation, we, the tourists, must respect the natural world, and use the most powerful vote of all — the money in our pockets — to effect a change for the better in the tourist industry.

Hanna Bolus

How to be an Environmentally Responsible Tourist

When we go on holiday we take for granted our right to invade an environment not our own. But whether we are visiting one of Britain's national parks, or a more remote destination, there is plenty we can do to minimize the negative environmental impact of our visit, and even turn it into a positive influence. Consumer pressure is perhaps the most powerful influence for change, so each of us can make a difference.

● *Before choosing your holiday, ask the tour operator for its green credentials. There are plenty of 'green' package tours available.*

● *Investigate terms such as 'ecotourism' and 'environmentally friendly tourism'.*

Many tourism watchdogs now exist including Green Flag International which awards a symbol to participating tour operators for showing regard for the landscape and wildlife. The environmental charity Ark launched the Green Travel Bug campaign to expose environmental concerns about tourism. The organization Tourism Concern can also provide helpful advice.

● *Consider a working holiday. In Britain, organizations such as the National Trust and British Trust for Conservation Volunteers (BTCV) both offer conservation holiday schemes.*

● *When on holiday abroad make sure you treat the environment with consideration: do not pick wild flowers, try to conserve water and energy, and support the local economy by buying locally-made souvenirs. Dissuade others from buying wildlife trinkets, such as coral, ivory, and snake skins.*

PROBLEMS IN PARADISE

Above: *The Galapagos sea lion thrives on the islands' coasts.*

Far right: *The Galapagos hawk, the islands' only bird of prey, makes use of an unconventional landing pad.*

Below: *Volcanoes have given rise to spectacular landscapes.*

The Galapagos Islands are unlike anywhere else on earth. Their black, rocky lava shores are remarkably inhospitable to life. Much of the land is very dry for most of the year and, except on three or four islands, fresh water is scarce or absent.

Yet this strange archipelago, lying on the Equator nearly 960km from the mainland of South America, fascinates adventurers, scientists and, today, tourists. One of the first to experience its magic was Charles Darwin, who spent a few weeks there in 1835. Later he was to write: 'Here, both in space and time, we seem to be brought somewhat near to that great fact — that mystery of mysteries — the first appearance of new beings on this earth.' The animals that Darwin found on the islands gave an early clue that eventually led to his theory of evolution. The islands thus played a pivotal role in the shaping of modern biology, and a new way of understanding the world. But that does not make them a Garden of Eden. The American writer Herman Melville, who visited Galapagos in 1841, was not impressed. He described them in a short novel as 'a group rather of extinct volcanoes than of isles, looking much as the world at large might have looked after a penal conflagration'.

Nevertheless, the popular view of these distant islands conjures up a wildlife paradise. And in its way, it is. The animals that live there, especially the birds and reptiles, have evolved in a world essentially without predators or — until recently — humans. They are remarkably unafraid, and seem to thrive in this apparently harsh environment.

Today the Galapagos Islands are famous on two other counts. Thanks to timely action about 30 years ago, they have become a triumph of nature conservation. At the same time, they are renowned as a shining example of how to integrate conservation with responsible tourism.

The need to conserve the islands first became publicized in the 1950s, when a young German zoologist, Irenäus Eibl-Eibesfeldt, reported that giant tortoises were being killed for food and their young sold as pets; sea lions and native birds were being shot for sport, and introduced domestic animals were running wild and destroying the native plants and animals.

His report led to the establishment in 1959 of the Charles Darwin Foundation for the Galapagos Islands (CDF), an independent, international body set up to help the government of Ecuador protect the islands. Despite this positive step forward, it was clearly important for a national park to be established in the islands. The groundwork for this was laid in 1966 and included the recommendation that tourists should travel between the islands by boat or ship, and sleep aboard; and that they should be accompanied on shore by trained guides.

This policy meant that no facilities needed to be built in the national park. It also provided an income for the boat operators and guides. Most importantly, it meant that the guides would not only act as war-

Below: *Land iguanas obtain nourishment from the abundant cacti.*

dens and 'control' the tourists, but would add to their enjoyment by giving them in-depth information about the wildlife. The system works admirably, and has been copied in parks and reserves around the world.

The Galapagos National Park covers about 8000sq km, or 97 per cent of the land area of the islands. The only land excluded is that which was already occupied by settlers in 1969. The human inhabitants of Galapagos adjusted quite quickly to the idea of not disturbing the native wildlife. Most of them were happy to benefit from the income generated by the gradually increasing number of visitors. But the conservationists had other problems, such as controlling the introduced animals and plants which were threatening the native species. These animals include dogs, cats, rats, house mice, goats, pigs, donkeys, horses, cattle, and even scarab beetles and fire ants. Some of these will never be eradicated on some islands, due to a combination of the rugged terrain and the sheer survival skills of the animals themselves.

There have been successes: dogs and pigs have been greatly reduced, and goats, the most destructive of all the exotics, have been eliminated from five islands, but their astonishing reproductive potential is well illustrated on Pinta Island. Three goats were released there, as a future food supply, by fishermen in 1957. By 1968 the population had reached 10–15,000, and a mere three years after that the total had soared to around 25,000. Thankfully, park service personnel have managed to eliminate most of these, and the vegetation is growing back steadily. But it is a tough and costly battle that is far from over.

The native vegetation of Galapagos is just as special as the islands' many unique animal species. Yet these plants are not only threatened by the introduced animals, but also by the steady spread of plants and trees brought by the settlers in the last century. Some of the intruders are food plants, some ornamental or medicinal, and some are trees that provide building materials. Seeds, too, have been brought in accidentally. All told, there are more than 260 introduced plant species.

The introduced plants are generally more successful than the native species, starving them of sunlight, water, and nutrients. Some of these are extremely damaging. Lantana, brought to Floreana Island to beautify a family garden, now covers 20sq km, its seeds dispersed by the native Darwin's finches and by introduced rats. It forms dense thickets, and prevents the endangered dark-rumped petrel from entering its nesting burrows.

Passion fruit vines climb native trees and block out the sun, guava trees have formed large forests covering 400sq km, while red quinine trees are spreading through the

unique Miconia vegetation zone in the highlands of Santa Cruz Island. In most cases, it is extremely difficult to eradicate introduced plants. As with the alien animals, the best that can probably be hoped for is to contain their spread.

There is, however, good news to balance this catalogue of problems. Two decades of captive breeding of reptiles by biologists, helped by parks personnel, have been remarkably successful. More than a thousand captive-reared giant tortoises have been released on their ancestral islands, and most of the 11 surviving subspecies of these famous creatures are being re-established. Unfortunately, little can be done for the Pinta Island tortoise, as only one male, nicknamed 'Lonesome George', survives. Of special note is the Hood Island race, which has a saddle-shaped carapace. Only two elderly males and 11 females remained in the 1960s, and these were so widely dispersed that they never met. Now, some 250

Above: *Lumbering and helpless, giant tortoises were sitting targets for hungry sailors and settlers. They enjoy a safer future today, playing a starring role among Galapagos' many tourist attractions.*

Left: *In the cloud forests of Santa Cruz island, tree-dwelling vegetation festoons the branches. Some two-thirds of Galapagos' plant species are found nowhere else in the world.*

young tortoises have been returned to the island, where they should soon be breeding. Biologists at the station have achieved equally promising results with land iguanas, having bred and re-introduced three endangered subspecies.

In the last century, sealers almost wiped out the Galapagos fur seal, but thanks to strict protection in recent decades, they number about 40,000 today. Pacific green turtles are doing well, too, with thousands returning each year to lay their eggs on pristine Galapagos beaches. There was a scare in the early 1970s when a Japanese refrigerator ship arrived and, with local help, collected large numbers. But the Darwin station director at the time, Peter Kramer, persuaded the Ecuadorian government to ban this commercial exploitation indefinitely. Recently, two new difficulties have arisen. When the national park was established, planners estimated that up to 12,000 tourists a year could visit without harming the environment. There were virtually none at that time, but numbers increased during the 1970s as the wonders of Galapagos became widely known. By 1984, about 20,000 people were coming to the islands each year. Then, suddenly, there was a rise to over 40,000 in 1988. The figure is now nudging 50,000.

The authorities are now trying to make this the upper limit, mainly by refusing to issue any more boat licences. But the local Ecuadorian population is expanding, and there is a demand to allow more boats in

*Below: **Penguins dart and twist after a shoal of panicked prey. Scientists are extremely concerned that a slump in the Galapagos fish stocks may put entire food chains at risk.***

order to provide more jobs. The park has so far absorbed visitors without significant evidence of stress, but at some point the environment will suffer and the quality of the experience will be degraded for the visitors.

A bigger problem, however, is that many people have been arriving on the islands from the mainland of Ecuador in the hope of exploiting the tourist boom. Today some 12,000 people live there, mainly on Santa Cruz and San Cristobal Islands, but the land available is strictly limited and therefore very expensive. Pressure is mounting to release some land from the national park to accommodate these people, many of whom do not understand the fragile link between conservation and tourism.

Another alarming trend is the over-exploitation of marine resources. Unlike the land, the waters of Galapagos were not protected until the creation of a 70,000sq km Marine Resources Reserve in 1986. This covers all of the archipelago, up to 15 nautical miles offshore. In 1992, the outer limit was extended to 80 miles for foreign fishing vessels. But because of the different ministries claiming jurisdiction — those involved with the law of the sea, defence, tourism, fisheries, and development — it has proved hard to agree how to regulate activities within the reserve, and protective policies are hard to enforce. For example, the large groupers known locally as bacalao are much sought after by fishermen, but catches have steadily declined in weight and size of fish. Nowadays, 70 per cent of the bacalao landed are immature, and fishermen are also taking lobsters below the legal size, including females with eggs. Nor are close seasons properly observed.

Foreign fishing vessels, mostly Japanese, Korean, and Taiwanese, are now reportedly waiting outside the exclusion zone, while local or mainland-based boats fish on their behalf. The development of large-scale commercial fishing threatens whales and

Above: *The waved albatross breeds almost exclusively on Hood Island in the Galapagos.*

dolphins, sea lions and fur seals, and a host of seabirds such as tropicbirds, frigatebirds, boobies, and the rare Galapagos penguins and flightless cormorants.

Ecuador has now enacted most of the laws necessary to control exploitation of Galapagos waters. However, the Galapagos National Park service has neither the money nor the manpower to take more than token action, and the navy's pair of 30-knot patrol vessels can do little in an area of 70,000sq km. Meanwhile, divers report that hammerhead and other sharks are now hard to find in areas where they were once plentiful. This may be just the tip of the iceberg.

The Charles Darwin Foundation is pressurizing the Ecuadorian government to set up a properly funded management authority for the marine reserve. It is lobbying for prompt action to stop the plunder of marine resources, which are just as significant as the terrestrial wildlife of the archipelago. For if the degradation of Galapagos is allowed to continue it will have tragic consequences not only for this island paradise but for the natural world as a whole.

Nigel Sitwell

Overleaf: *Marine iguanas throng Galapagos' coasts — both above and below the hissing surf.*

WILDLIFE
& CONSERVATION
ORGANIZATIONS

It is usually the dramatic conservation stories

that hit the news — a rescue attempt on an endangered animal, or a

confrontation with ruthless poachers. But we hear little of the

conservationists themselves, and our knowledge of the laws that

govern their activities is probably even less.

This section begins by looking at current conservation

work in Belize, where protecting one species — the jaguar — has

benefited this beautiful country's wildlife as a whole. In Britain, the

RSPB has been dedicated to bird conservation for over a hundred

years, and is the model for similar organizations all over the world.

The Marine Conservation Society's successes with aquatic wildlife

have been more recent, but are no less impressive.

There is an overview of the laws that help to protect

the world's wildlife, and an explanation of the recent shake-up in

the former Nature Conservancy Council. Finally, we go inside one of

the world's highest-profile conservation groups, Greenpeace.

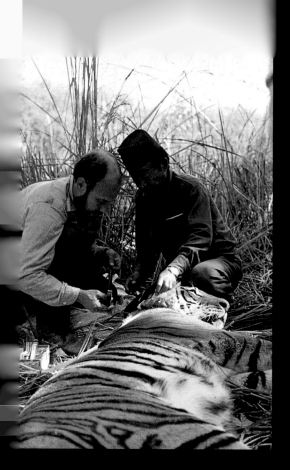

Above left: *Trained conservationists must combine forces with local people to make conservation projects an ongoing success.*

Above: *Observation is as important as intervention in the monitoring of rare or threatened species.*

Left: *1992 has not been an easy year for the International Whaling Commission, and it is vital that conservation organizations continue to campaign on behalf of these beleaguered marine mammals.*

JAGUARS IN THE JUNGLE

Above: A praying mantis lurks on bougainvillaea leaves in the Belizean forest, waiting to snatch its insect prey.

Far right: This young jaguar relieves the irritation of teething by gnawing on a branch.

Right: The voracious fer-de-lance consumes a frog head-first. After such a meal, it will be some time before the snake needs to eat again.

As it stands in the undergrowth by a forest trail, the stocky body and large head of the jaguar are all but invisible. Its golden coat, dappled with black rosettes, melts into the early morning shadows and the light filtering through the leaves. Cautiously, it emerges and walks down the track with a heavy, almost ungainly step before disappearing again into the rainforest.

The jaguar typically inhabits lowland jungles near rivers but has been seen in the mountains of Bolivia and Peru. Its range once stretched from the USA south as far as Uruguay and Argentina, but its numbers are now drastically reduced. Since 1973 it has been classified as vulnerable to extinction.

Hunting has played a part in the jaguar's decline, as its coat has been prized for thousands of years, by ancient Mayan priests and modern furriers alike. Before trade in its fur was banned, up to 39,000 jaguars were killed each year and some hunting continues illegally today. But the greatest threat to the jaguar comes from the clearing of its forest habitat for timber and to make space for farms and human settlements.

It is hard to assess how critical the jaguar's situation has become because no-one knows the size of former or current populations. So why has this big cat been so little studied? The chief reason is that its

forest habitats are often hard for researchers to penetrate, and long-term projects have been made more dangerous by the political instability of many of its native countries. The jaguar's habits make study even more difficult: it is a solitary beast with a large territory, and tends to hunt at dusk and dawn. It is not surprising that until 10 years ago very little was known about the life and habits of this beautiful creature.

People's attitudes are slowly changing and in some places, real efforts are now being made to study and protect the jaguar. In the small Central American country of Belize, there is still a healthy jaguar population. In 1984 the Cockscomb Basin Jaguar Preserve was opened in woodland previously logged for timber. Other forest reserves have also been established and the country now has an impressive and varied network of conservation areas.

Belize, which was a British colony until 1981, relies increasingly on tourism for its national income and its commitment to conservation has attracted many thousands of visitors to its nature reserves. By protecting the jaguar, Belize is safeguarding its tourist industry, but it is also saving the forest and hence the many other creatures that live there. Stretches of land which would probably have been cleared for crops and cattle farming will now be left in their natural state.

In 1988 a charity called the Programme For Belize (PFB) was founded with a grant from the Massachusetts Audubon Society. Its aim was to help solve the problems that arise when the needs of people conflict with those of their environment. Much of Belize's land is privately owned, and the PFB's original plan was to buy a stretch of suitable forest and protect it in perpetuity using a land management plan.

Above: *The limpid-eyed margay is the smallest of Belize's spotted cats. Very little is known about the habits of this shy, nocturnal creature.*

been graded into zones. Zone One areas are left wild; Zone Two areas are set aside for wildlife observation and research. Zone Three land will eventually be harvested selectively for wood, medicinal plants and chicle (used in chewing gum), while Zone Four land will be used for tourist facilities and archaeological research. Income from harvests and tourism will subsidize the cost of running the nature reserve.

In Britain, people are offered the chance to 'buy' an acre of rainforest for £25. This idea has met with great enthusiasm. Grants from the USA are also funding three rangers and a research station manager. This is important because people have been found illegally setting up home in the reserve and growing crops there, and chicle is being stolen from some of the trees. Ruined Mayan temples which have been discovered in the reserve must also be protected until they can be properly explored.

Cooperating with local people in running a reserve can be problematic but it works well most of the time. Belizeans are proud of their natural heritage, and the level of literacy is high, so it is easy to publicize the work of the country's reserves. Belize is about the size of Wales, but its population is only 250,000, so the overcrowding which often drives people to clear rainforests in other parts of Central and South America does not exist here. It is a very stable country politically, which also helps.

The Community Baboon Sanctuary is a good example of local involvement in conservation. In 1985, 11 land-owners pledged to manage their lands to benefit the declining populations of the howler monkey, known in Belize as the baboon. They left strips of forest on the borders of property and did not cut down the fruit trees the monkey prefers. Where roads and clearings separated trees, they even rigged up aerial walkways. Soon, visitors began to arrive.

More than a hundred land-owners from

This would employ local people to use the land in ways that were both sustainable and harmless to the resident wildlife.

Funds were raised in Britain and the USA and in 1990, 445sq km of forest in the Rio Bravo area was purchased, forming the core of the Rio Bravo Conservation and Management Area. Adjoining it is another 526sq km area which is privately owned but managed on similar lines, and a further 372sq km donated by Coca-Cola Foods in two parts, in 1990 and 1992.

The various areas fit together like a jigsaw in the northwestern corner of Belize. Much of it is prime tropical forest, filled with monkeys, tapirs, pumas, jaguars, peccaries and countless birds, including toucans, motmots and king vultures. Many areas have been selectively logged for years, but these stretches of secondary forest are still lush and beautiful. The reserve has, however, different villages are now involved, with some people offering bed and breakfast to tourists. The result for the villagers is a steady income, while visitors get a rare glimpse of rural Belize. Sometimes during the day, and especially at dawn and dusk, the howler monkeys steal the show with their phenomenal cacophony; the sound of rival troops bellowing at each other can be heard over a kilometre away. Thanks to the sanctuary, between 1985 and 1988 the local howler population increased from about 840 animals to more than a thousand.

Sadly, the Community Baboon Sanctuary covers only a small area, and howler monkeys elsewhere take their chances with an enemy far more deadly than any natural predator — forest clearance.

Large reserves, however, can sustain vast numbers of species. The Rio Bravo Conservation Area is just one of several in Belize. The Mountain Pine Ridge Reserve is the only place in the country where the rare orange-breasted falcon can be found. The

Crooked Tree Wildlife Sanctuary is wetland, important as a feeding station for birds, while the Hol Chan Marine Reserve lies off the coast of Ambergris Cay. There, visitors can peer at Belize's barrier reef through diving masks or glass-hulled boats. The Half Moon Cay Reserve, on the outer reaches of the reef, contains many seabirds, including a colony of 4000 red-footed boobies. The Cockscomb Basin Jaguar Preserve, set up to preserve jaguars, also contains thousands of other species.

In the forests where it lives, the jaguar is at the top of the food chain. It eats just about anything it can catch, varying its diet according to the seasons of the year and its habitat. Peccaries are a favourite food, but these bristly-haired, pig-like mammals can be extremely fierce. The jaguar picks off young or old peccaries if they stray but would be unwilling to tackle an entire herd.

Above: *Off the coast of Belize, the rare American manatee cruises the warm waters it prefers. This totally aquatic mammal benefits from protected marine areas.*

Left: *Exquisite plant species such as the black orchid abound in the lush humidity of Belize's tropical forests.*

127

Frequently, it opts for smaller, easier prey animals such as anteaters, iguanas, pacas and agoutis, although it means hunting more often. According to Melanie Watt, an expert on Belizean jaguars, it has been reported eating 'everything from avocados to anacondas'. Armadillos also feature heavily in the 80 or so recorded prey species.

The jaguar is locally known as *el tigre,* but its true name comes from *yaquara* in the South American Tupi-Guarani language, which means 'wild beast that overcomes its prey in a single bound'. This exactly describes the way it hunts. In relation to its size, the jaguar has the most powerful jaws in the cat family. It kills by biting through the back of the prey's neck or skull, but if it is hunting a large animal it leaps on to its back and throws it off-balance by hauling the head round sideways with its paw.

There are many stories of unprovoked jaguar attacks on humans, but of all the big cats it has the smallest reputation as a man-eater. The jaguar is more likely to come into conflict with local people if it develops a taste for cattle. This occurs most frequently with injured jaguars. Under normal circumstances, the jaguar is reluctant to cross open ground, so livestock are safe unless they are kept by the edge of the forest. Jaguars have often been blamed for cattle theft when the culprit was human.

The jaguar shares its territory with many other cat species. The ocelot, margay, puma and jaguarundi are found with jaguars in many of Belize's forest reserves and the ranges of male jaguars may overlap; scent and claw marks are used to warn off intruders and avoid potentially fatal fights.

The most frequently hunted cat in Latin America is the ocelot, or 'tiger-cat' as it is known in Belize. It can weigh up to 15kg and has a beautiful striped and spotted coat which makes it a much coveted prize even though it is a threatened species.

Above: *Belize's invertebrates, such as the exquisite malachite butterfly, benefit from various conservation projects that preserve land from clearance.*

Right: *The female black howler monkey lacks the bony chamber in its throat that amplifies the male's astonishing calls.*

It is notoriously difficult to identify animals in the rainforest, and when distance makes it hard to guess size an ocelot may be identified by hopeful eyes as a jaguar.

It is even harder to tell an ocelot from a margay. The margay is the smallest spotted cat in Belize and the one about which least is known. It is a very arboreal cat, gracefully built and slimmer than the ocelot, with a relatively longer tail. It is hunted for its fur and is also trapped for the pet market.

There is still a need for ongoing conservation work in Belize. A team of scientists from the Natural History Museum in London has been surveying an area in the Upper Raspaculo region in the Maya Mountains. It is the first time the mammals of this area have been studied and a great number of species have been identified from sightings, tracks and droppings. These include southern river otters and the rare Baird's tapir. Tapirs live on a diet of many different leaves and can weigh up to 300kg.

They are easily recognized by their long, overhanging snout. The tapir is Belize's national animal, so it is especially important to preserve those populations surviving in the wild.

In 1980, the World Wildlife Fund (now the World Wide Fund for Nature) warned that the jaguar could be extinct within 20 years. The work of scientists and the government of Belize may have stabilized its decline there just in time, for the jaguar breeds fast in the right conditions and populations can then recover. The growth of eco-tourism in Belize is a strong weapon in the battle to preserve those which are left.

One of the difficulties of promoting visits to rainforest reserves is the probability that the tourists will not see any big, glamorous animals. Belize cannot compete with safari tours on the plains of Africa, where the animals live in the open. Instead, it can offer a sense of real adventure, the thrill of following tracks, of smelling the forest, hearing strange noises and seeing shapes in every shadow. For a lucky few, there will also be the magical moment when they look back along a trail and their gaze is met by a pair of inquisitive, bright yellow eyes.

Sarah Foster

Left: *Although trade in ocelot fur is banned under international law, a certain amount of poaching still threatens this endangered cat.*

Below: *The keel-billed toucan is one of the many colourful species which make a visit to Belize an attractive prospect for an increasing number of 'eco-tourists'.*

STRICTLY FOR THE BIRDS

Right: *Although the snipe is in no immediate danger, the continued destruction of its wetland habitat could lead to its decline.*

Far right: *The avocet died out in Britain in the last century when it was hunted for food. When two breeding colonies were subsequently discovered in Suffolk, the RSPB established two coastal reserves, and numbers swelled to 385 pairs by 1988.*

Below: *The success of the RSPB's first campaign to save the avocet in 1947 led to its adoption as the Society's symbol.*

The Royal Society for the Protection of Birds — the RSPB — is the best known and largest wildlife organization in the UK. It is also the largest such organization in Europe and is on its way to becoming one of the largest in the world. For 104 years the RSPB has been working for wild birds and their habitats. Today, with nearly 900,000 members, it owes its success to two ingredients: the universal appeal of birds, and the efficient way it runs its affairs.

The RSPB started, like many organizations, when a few people came together and decided that 'something must be done'. The few people were a group of women in a small town outside Manchester, and the 'something' was stopping the cruel trade in bird feathers. Wild birds were being killed in their thousands to supply the hat industry. The RSPB's first leaflet, *Destruction of Ornamentally Plumaged Birds*, helped to raise awareness of the birds' plight, and led to them getting the protection they needed. The RSPB was under way.

The RSPB has grown from a small voluntary organization into a medium-sized business. Although volunteers still play a vital role, there are over 750 full-time, professional members of staff.

According to Gillian Stacey, the RSPB's Campaign Manager, the Society's role is 'to protect wild birds and their habitats'. This is by no means a simple task. It involves research, campaigning, land purchase, educational work and publicity. It requires discussion with politicians to make sure that the law protects birds and their habitats. And it involves working with other people — from teachers to the police — to ensure that the RSPB is not working alone to encourage the appreciation and protection of Britain's birds.

Ever since it first came to the aid of birds threatened by feather hunters, the RSPB's work has involved vigorous campaigning. Its 1992 campaign was one of the largest and most ambitious ever undertaken for wildlife and the countryside. This was the RSPB Campaign for the Countryside, a bid to reclaim land for wildlife that is now used for agriculture.

Efficient modern farming methods have created vast, machine-friendly landscapes without the ponds, banks or hedges which once provided valuable havens for wildlife. And each year taxpayers subsidize the agricultural industry to produce food in just this way. But much of this food is never needed and ends up as part of the infamous EC grain mountains and wine lakes. This wasteful system, which has disastrous consequences for wildlife, angers conservationists and farmers alike.

The 1992 Campaign for the Countryside included the Million Image Challenge, intended to stimulate public interest in Britain's rural heritage. The Challenge was aimed at the politicians who shape the European Common Agricultural Policy, which provides the rules and regulations

on food production and prices. The RSPB needed to present a strong case to delegates at the Heads of Government Summit in December 1992, and to the Agricultural Commissioner in Brussels early in 1993. Their idea was to invite a million members of the public to send to the RSPB their own favourite image of the countryside — a drawing, painting, poem or country recipe — to show ministers that the people of Britain were concerned for the future of the nation's wildlife.

Instead of making a living simply by growing as much produce as possible, farmers would earn money from maintaining or creating habitats for plants and animals, such as ponds or meadows. The RSPB calculated that, with public pressure swaying decisions over agricultural land use, several hundred thousand hectares could be transformed in this way without any burden on the taxpayer.

Habitat conservation is not the RSPB's only role. There are times when particular species — and even individual birds — need active help from the Society. The osprey is one of the best-known species to receive help from the RSPB. Only a couple of decades ago ospreys, like red kites, were barely surviving as British breeding birds. The RSPB's efforts to protect their habitat, keep egg-collectors at bay and persuade gamekeepers not to persecute them have opened up a much more positive future for these powerful and exciting fish hunters.

British law aims to protect all birds, from ospreys and red kites to blackbirds and blue tits. But laws can have no effect without enforcement. The RSPB's small team of investigators work closely with police both in the UK and abroad to ensure that effective enforcement takes place.

In Thetford Forest, East Anglia, goshawk nests were being raided for their eggs. This was not the work of amateur egg-collectors, but of professional thieves carefully taking eggs to hatch, in order to sell the young goshawks for falconry. RSPB investigators and the police set up a 'stake-out' near a goshawk's nest, and after only a few hours' wait a man was arrested climbing the tree as he tried to raid the nest. Similar successes were achieved at eagle eyries in Scotland.

The 'bird detectives', as the investigators are affectionately known within the RSPB, have more than egg thieves to deal with. They have also helped to stop the illegal

poisoning of birds of prey — and have even found themselves filming secretly in an East London pub, where songbirds taken from the wild were being sold.

Incidents like these have led to convictions and fines as high as £6000. 'The police are keen to help,' says investigator Andy Jones, 'but quite understandably they are not always experts on birds. So we must be their eyes and ears.'

Andy and his colleague Karen Bradbury have made several visits to tropical countries to help stamp out the trade in cage birds. Beautiful birds such as parrots and cockatoos are illegally exported for the pet trade, often in tiny, cramped boxes. Many die before they end their journey.

On one occasion Andy and Karen set up a bogus trading company in Thailand to infiltrate the closed world of the bird dealers. They managed to film and tape the activities in one major trader's premises and were able to present their material to the Deputy Prime Minister. It may take some time, but the bird detectives believe that the wild bird trade will eventually end. Their work has already persuaded many major airlines to refuse to carry wild birds.

In view of the adventures of the RSPB investigators it is perhaps surprising that the RSPB has a slightly 'fuddy-duddy' image among some conservationists. This may be because, in comparison with other, more militant environmental organizations, the

Below: *The RSPB reserve at Haweswater in the Lake District is home to a spectacular array of birds, including a pair of golden eagles.*

RSPB's public activities seem to be a little tame — no climbing Nelson's Column or confronting whaling ships on the high seas in small inflatable dinghies.

The RSPB's work, as Gillian Stacey says, is 'carried out within the system. If that means people calling us fuddy-duddy, fine. But the point is that we do get results'. The RSPB aims to use careful arguments and tactful persuasion to get politicians, land-owners and the public on the side of the birds. It cannot afford to risk its reputation of moderation. If it did, politicians might take a less sympathetic view of it, and so might its members.

The RSPB is trying to involve a wider range of people, especially younger people. The RSPB Young Ornithologist's Club (YOC) is, at 120,000 strong, the largest wildlife organization for young people in the world. Since RSPB staff frequently visit schools to give talks, and since there are over a thousand YOC groups actually based in schools, there is no doubt that the RSPB is now reaching a wider audience.

Schools abroad also benefit from the RSPB's work, through its international department. 'As a British-based organization there is a limit to what we can do abroad,' says Dorothy Bashford, the RSPB's International Training Coordinator. 'But we can supply help and advice to bird protection organizations in other countries if they need it.'

Among the most successful projects the RSPB has helped overseas are the Wildlife Clubs of Ghana. Originally set up in a few schools with RSPB support to help educate children about threatened seabirds, the clubs have become extremely successful. There are now over a hundred of them and a permanent staff member tours the schools, taking children out to watch and learn about birds.

All this work would be impossible if the Society was not well run. The RSPB is a charity, and depends on the public's good will — and money — to enable it to do its job. Unlike a commercial business, it is not allowed to make profits for the people who run it. But like a business, it has to make its way in a competitive world. The staff put in a tremendous amount of effort and dedication, ensuring that members and donors get every penny's worth. Publicity is of paramount importance, and press briefings are a regular occurrence.

Barbara Young, the RSPB Chief Executive, sums it up: 'If you want a professional job done, you have to employ professional people and do everything in a businesslike manner. That is the way of the world, and it is the way we have to operate to do what we are here to do — work for birds'.

Tony Hare

BUYING PROTECTION

One of the main threats to birds is the destruction of their habitats. Many birds are adapted so specifically to their habitat that, if it is altered or removed, they simply cannot adapt to any other environment.

The RSPB resorts to one very simple way of protecting birds' habitats: it buys them. It is now one of Britain's biggest land-owners, with 119 reserves covering a total area twice the size of the Isle of Wight. The RSPB owns a third of the UK's reedbeds — essential habitats for many nesting birds — and RSPB reserves are home to over 60,000 of Britain's gannets — 17 per cent of the total population. At Haweswater, an RSPB reserve in the Lake District, the long list of occupants includes the common sandpiper, dipper, redstart, meadow pipit, raven, wood warbler, ring ouzel, buzzard, and the only breeding golden eagles in England.

The reserves are used for education as well as conservation: tens of thousands of school children use the Sandwell Valley reserve near Birmingham every year. Many of the reserves are run by wardens. According to Bob Scott, the RSPB's Head of Reserves Management, they have to be 'the ultimate jacks-of-all-trades'. They do everything from showing visitors around and counting fledglings to keeping the shop fully stocked and the money rolling in.

BEYOND THE BEACH

MARINE CONSERVATION SOCIETY

Above: *The Marine Conservation Society is working to make the 'seas fit for life'.*

Far right: *The squat shape of the edible crab is a familiar sight on the rocky shore.*

Below: *British seas may look grey and uninviting but a glimpse beneath the waves reveals a very different story.*

For most people in Britain, the sea is a treat to visit on holiday, to play beside or swim in; even sail on. Yet we are surrounded by seas and they have a profound impact upon our lives.

Four seas wash Britain's coasts: the North Sea, the English Channel, the Irish Sea and the vast Atlantic Ocean. They make oxygen, help regulate the climate and supply us with food and fuel. Most island peoples are skilled in sea-crafts and the British have been no exception, using ships for transport, fishing and defence.

For centuries, we have taken what we needed from the seas in ever-increasing amounts, but until very recently few of us considered whether marine resources could be sustained. Even now, it is hard to make people care about our own coast — tropical coral reefs seem far more important.

Yet it is a mistake to think our cold grey seas are dull or empty: they teem with life, from minute plankton to seals, dolphins and basking sharks — and this rich heritage needs protection. To do just this, in 1977 the Underwater Conservation Society (UCS) was formed, becoming the Marine Conservation Society (MCS) in 1983.

When the UCS was founded, official marine nature reserves simply did not exist: anything below the high tide mark had no legal protection. In 1981 it persuaded the government to include this new idea in the Wildlife and Countryside Act, and five years later Lundy Island was finally designated Britain's first statutory Marine Nature Reserve. It was not until 1990, however, that Skomer Island, off the Welsh coast, received the same legal protection from the government; far too slow an act in the eyes of the MCS, considering that Britain has more than 11,000km of coastline. In the meantime, the Society has helped to set up nine voluntary reserves around the country.

Adequate protection has yet to be established for the present Marine Nature Reserves, which are vulnerable because they cover such small areas. A much better idea would be to have large reserves containing areas with different degrees of protection. A carefully managed outer zone, still used for limited fishing and recreation, could act as a buffer for a more strictly protected inner reserve. In showing people that protected areas can benefit them as well as the marine environment, the MCS is changing negative attitudes which have been slowing progress. The success of voluntary reserves shows in miniature how such ideas can work.

'Seas Fit for Life' is the goal of the MCS, and is also the name of an appeal which it launched in 1991 to raise £450,000 to fund a wide-reaching conservation and education programme and to step up campaigns for the future. Progress is hampered, however, by the lack of any single organization responsible for the coast; the different

Far right: *Despite their bright colouring, many sea slugs pass for growths of sponge or fragments of seaweed.*

Below: *Yarrell's blenny lurks among kelp fronds. Its large eyes and the pair of divided tentacles on its head give it an endearing, comical expression.*

groups rarely work together or even know what the others are doing. The Society's biggest campaign for 1993 is supporting the introduction of a nationwide Coastal Zone Management (CZM) plan. It is working with the Department of the Environment and also encouraging local authorities nationwide to formulate CZM policies for their own regions. With one organization to oversee all uses of the coast, from fishing and tourism to industry and conservation, valuable sites can be properly protected.

Today, the MCS has nearly 6000 members, and continues to swell in numbers. In its aims to raise public awareness and educate people about the sea, it has accomplished a great deal since its foundation. It

has gained respect for its achievements and its method of quiet persuasion rather than dramatic confrontation. Well known for its scientific research, it is often consulted by government ministers.

Some matters can be dealt with only by government, though, and one of these is pollution. The sewage of some 31 million people empties into the North Sea — about 7.3 million cubic metres a day, much of which is untreated since outfalls serving less than 10,000 people are legally allowed to discharge raw sewage. With help from local volunteers, the MCS monitors Britain's coast and publishes *The Good Beach Guide* every year (see box). It has made a tremendous difference in Britain by involving ordinary

people in practical conservation. The biggest project involving voluntary support is Coastwatch UK, sponsored by Norwich Union. This is an annual 'snapshot' survey of the entire British coastline which takes place over two weeks every autumn. Thousands of individuals take part and the MCS also enlists help from hundreds of schools, clubs and other groups around the country which send in information about their nearest stretch of coast.

Local schemes have met with much success, but seas cannot be contained by national borders, and problems on one side of an ocean may well spread. Over the years, the MCS has done much to highlight threats to habitats and individual species worldwide. The MCS's most important tool is its flexibility. On the one hand it is working with British and European governments at international conferences discussing issues like alternative sewage treatment, while on the other it welcomes help from anyone willing to volunteer. Over the years, it has proved itself helpful, positive and well-informed; just the kind of ally needed to protect our seas.

Sarah Foster

COME ON IN, THE WATER'S LOVELY!

Every year the MCS assesses the standard of beaches around Britain and rates them on a one to four star rating system, which is based on the European Community Bathing Water Directive (1976).

Under this law some 450 designated bathing waters have been identified in Britain. These are regularly monitored for sewage pollution by the National Rivers Authority, River Purification Boards and the Department of the Environment, throughout the bathing season. Sadly, only 20 beaches throughout the whole of Britain qualified in 1992 for the MCS's 4 star rating. These sites are listed below and marked on our map. The full list of beaches, including those which have failed to meet the criteria of the EC Directive, is published in The Good Beach Guide.

1. Whitesands Bay, Lothian
2. Dunglass, Lothian
3. Benone, Northern Ireland
4. Cranfield, Northern Ireland
5. Porth Neigwl Beach, Gwynedd
6. Porth Ceriad Beach, Gwynedd
7. Crawley Woods, West Glamorgan
8. Rockham Bay, Devon
9. Woolacombe Sand, Devon
10. Shipload Bay, Devon
11. Welcombe Mouth, Devon
12. Porthoustock, Cornwall
13. St Anthony's Head, Cornwall
14. Portholland Beach, Cornwall
15. Vault Beach, Cornwall
16. Slapton Sands, Devon
17. Blackpool Sands, Devon
18. Chesil Beach, Dorset
19. Sandsfoot, Dorset
20. Durdle Door West, Dorset

INTERNATIONAL WILDLIFE LAW

Right: *The 1961 Antarctic Treaty aims to protect the vast, ownerless southern continent, but lacks the power to enforce its own well-intentioned rules.*

Below: *It is essential that any treaty aimed at conserving a species must include full protection of its habitat.*

We may worry about the future of rare species or rainforests, but few of us know how such issues are tackled legally from one country to another. What is the point, after all, of UK law protecting a migratory bird which then reaches its wintering grounds in Africa only to be shot? Wildlife protection needs to be on a worldwide basis to be effective. International environmental law is still a relatively new area, but it is showing how public concern and pressure can shape global legislation.

If countries want to form international rules for wildlife conservation, they list their obligations in a treaty. Treaties should require their signatories to review implementation regularly, and establish 'watchdog' bodies to check on and assist countries in implementing conservation measures. Countries are usually required to make the treaties part of their national law, so that their own authorities can, for example, confiscate illegally traded animals and plants and impose fines for such offences.

Some wildlife treaties were drawn up in reaction to the plight of a particular species. A good example of this was the fight to save the vicuña, a South American relative of the llama which was hunted almost to extinction due to world demand for its wool. The La Paz Agreement, signed in 1969 by five South American countries, prohibited the killing of the vicuña for its meat, skin or wool. Vicuña populations then recovered to the extent that Peru began a culling programme in 1977, claiming that the numbers had risen to such a level that some animals were starving. Other countries disputed the need for a cull. Consequently, the 1979

Right: *Irritated by the IWC bans, which they view as legalistic and outdated, the major whaling nations frequently breach international law.*

Below: *Despite international protection, the walrus is still killed for its magnificent ivory tusks, which can reach almost a metre in length.*

Lima Convention was drawn up to allow limited culling. These conventions not only banned hunting and international trade, but they also required signatories to conserve the vicuña's habitat. Most importantly, the treaties led to the creation of an international body to oversee vicuña conservation.

International law has also had some success in halting the slaughter of whales, most of which inhabit open sea beyond national boundaries. The International Convention for the Regulation of Whaling came into force in 1948. The treaty established the International Whaling Commission (IWC), which meets annually to adopt regulations concerning the numbers which can be caught and which species can be hunted.

In its early days, the IWC sought only to achieve the recovery of whale stocks so that

killing could recommence as before. Faced with dwindling stocks and growing public pressure, however, the IWC was forced to become more conservationist in approach.

The need for conservation became so critical that in 1982, the IWC prohibited any commercial whaling during the 1985–86 hunting season until further notice. The three main whaling states — Japan, Norway and the former USSR — objected to this, and whaling continued until 1988. The ban has therefore been in place for just over four years. But even during this period some countries have abused a provision in the treaty which permits whaling for scientific purposes. This loophole means that whale products can still be bought.

At the 43rd meeting of the IWC in 1991, the whaling nations attempted to overturn the ban on commercial whaling. The following year Iceland formally left the IWC and founded its own whaling organization. The hunting of whales is still a contentious issue but, among most participating countries, it seems that the original objective of the IWC treaty — to allow continued

on identifying, and stopping trade in, endangered species. This was signed in 1975, and now has 133 states party to it.

It is easy to see the problems involved in implementing international wildlife law in a case like the CITES ban on the ivory trade. The African elephant was given Appendix 1 (maximum) protection by CITES in 1989, ending the trade in ivory which had put the species' survival at risk. At the annual conference of parties to CITES in March 1992, five African states requested that restricted trade be allowed to resume. They argue that there must be some trade to make it worthwhile — and economically possible — for their people to conserve the elephant.

Other states are against this, saying that resuming any sort of trade opens up the market to poachers as well as legitimate traders. But those states which endorse the ban must be prepared to send money both for conservation programmes and to compensate the affected African countries for lost trade. Otherwise, these countries are likely to pull out of the treaty, leaving no protection for the elephant.

exploitation — is giving way to an ideal that is more sympathetic towards whales.

One of the more successful treaties for wildlife protection has been the Convention on International Trade in Endangered Species (CITES), which originally focused

Left: *The 1979 Lima Convention safeguards the future of the vicuña's habitat in the high-altitude grassland of the Andes.*

143

Right: *Legislation arrived none too soon for the snow leopard and its coveted coat. This cat lives in remote regions where poaching is very hard to control.*

Wildlife treaties do not just aid specific species, but also seek to protect habitats. The international treaty for the protection of European habitats is the Convention on the Conservation of European Wildlife and Natural Habitats — the Berne Convention — effective from 1982. Signatories to this treaty undertake to conserve wildlife and wildlife habitats in general and to provide special protection for species. Countries signing the treaty must also take measures to maintain populations of all species of animals and plants at levels corresponding to ecological, scientific and cultural requirements — even if this means sacrificing economic interests.

The treaty provides the all-important watchdog organization, regular meetings of the parties and reporting requirements.

The non-governmental organizations (NGOs) have a key role both in developing international environmental legislation and in ensuring its enforcement. Environmental NGOs are not recognized in international law — they cannot take a country to court — but they do attend conferences involving both the negotiations and drafting of treaties. The World Conservation Union (IUCN) played a major role in the initiation and drafting of CITES, and Greenpeace International has been involved in the negotiation of virtually all international environmental treaties in the past decade. There is little doubt that without the intervention of NGOs — and in particular the UK-based Environmental Investigation Agency — the decision to promote the African elephant to CITES Appendix 1 would not have taken place.

The role of the NGOs has shown that ordinary people can have a say in the making of environmental law. You could help in your own area by helping to protect the species listed under the Wildlife Act. Keep an eye out for any of the species listed and bring any abuse of them to the attention of English Nature, Scottish Natural Heritage or the Countryside Commission for Wales. Make sure that the traders in wildlife have no-one to sell to — do not buy ivory or exotic birds, for example. Another positive thing you can do is to support groups like the World Wide Fund for Nature, Friends of the Earth and Greenpeace — they really can and do help in the legal protection of the world's wildlife.

Despite the huge concern that many people feel for the future of the species sharing the planet with us, there is currently no worldwide treaty for the protection of habitats or ecosystems at risk. Last year's

Earth Summit in Rio proved that the economic interests of developed nations continue to override the need for conservation measures to safeguard wildlife for the future. Without the will of individual countries, international law alone cannot hope to provide the way.

Helen Clapperton

Above: *Ironically, some of the loudest voices calling for a resumption in ivory trading belong to a number of conservationists. The ivory ban, they say, leaves Africans with no financial motive for protecting the elephant.*

Left: *The deforestation of Indonesian islands is largely to blame for the babirusa's decline, despite its listing on CITES Appendix 1.*

CONSERVATION CARVE-UP

Until the 1990s, there was only one government body involved in nature conservation in Britain: the Nature Conservancy Council (NCC). The NCC was responsible for National Nature Reserves and other conservation sites; for liaising with government, farmers, foresters and other land-users; for helping voluntary bodies with money and advice; and for encouraging the public to take more interest in our wildlife.

That situation changed, however, when the government decided to split the NCC, as from April 1991, into three country agencies for England, Scotland and Wales, jointly supported by a fourth body. This may seem like a way of re-packaging the same body simply by using a lot more red tape. But to anybody concerned about the plants, animals and wild places of Britain, this split has important consequences.

Britain's first official conservation agency was Nature Conservancy, which was set up in 1949. Its objectives broadly divided into research into wildlife conservation, and the establishment and maintenance of nature reserves. Conservation in Northern Ireland was — and still is — the responsibility of the Northern Ireland Department of the Environment.

In 1973 the government decided to separate off the research function as a new body, the Institute of Terrestrial Ecology, and to give greater autonomy to the conservation part by establishing an independent council. And so the NCC was born.

The most public face of the NCC has always been its National Nature Reserves (NNRs), a collection of the most important wildlife areas in Britain which are managed

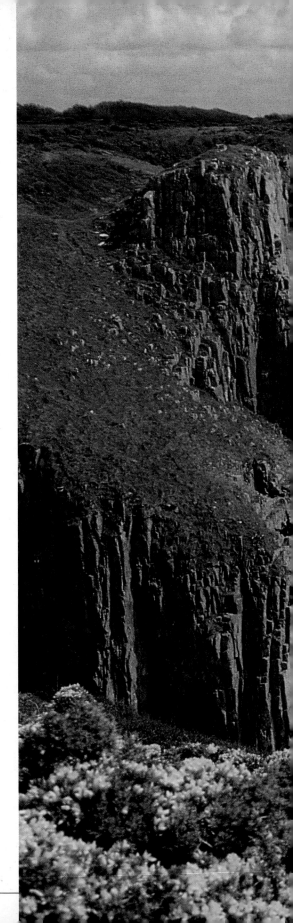

for the benefit of nature conservation. By March 1991, there were 242 NNRs across the country, totalling almost 1685sq km. Two Marine Nature Reserves had also been established in the sea around the islands of Lundy in the Bristol Channel and Skomer off the coast of Wales.

National Nature Reserves represent the crown jewels of British nature conservation. Among the richest areas for wildlife, they include some of the best examples of their type of habitat, such as oakwood, chalk down or freshwater marsh. Most are open to the public, but in the more delicate areas public access may be limited or even restricted to scientists.

The NCC also had limited powers over a second chain of sites, called Sites of Special Scientific Interest (SSSIs). These are pieces of privately owned land which contain richly varied or rare wildlife, and range in size from small ponds and woods to whole river systems or high plateaus. Sites with interesting geology or land forms are also likely candidates. By March 1991, there were more than 5600 SSSIs in Great Britain covering over 18,000sq km.

The NCC was responsible for liaising with the owners and occupiers of SSSIs, in order to limit potential damage through proposed agricultural schemes or other land alteration. Generally, SSSIs were protected on the basis of trust and voluntary agreements, perhaps with payments to help offset financial loss where the NCC had impeded the profit-making activities of farmers or other land-users.

The SSSI system has undoubtedly helped protect the most special wild places across Britain, but is by no means a guarantee of protection: a recent survey suggested that over a third of SSSIs have deteriorated or been damaged in recent years, and almost a quarter are threatened by future developments. It was the NCC's approach to one such threat which led directly to its demise.

In the mid-1980s, proposals emerged for large-scale forest planting in the Flow Country in the far northeast of Scotland. This vast area of undisturbed wet peatland, interspersed with pools and small lakes, is the breeding ground for birds such as golden plovers, dunlins, greenshanks, Arctic skuas and black-throated divers.

Concerned for the integrity of this special area of blanket bog, the NCC set about notifying large sections of it as SSSI. At the same time, members of the Council criticized the forestry plans, which were motivated largely by tax benefits. The Scottish Office, however, which controlled most forms of land-use in Scotland, resented the influence of a body funded by Westminster, and powerful voices called for local control of conservation in Scotland.

In the end, an unsatisfactory compromise was reached over the Flow Country that allowed half to be zoned for forestry and

Right: The JNCC helps to unify the national bodies — and international agencies — in research and conservation work. This is vital for projects on migrants such as that aimed at conserving the white-fronted goose, which involves the support of Greenland and Iceland.

half to be protected for conservation. Later, too, the discredited system of tax benefits for forestry was reformed, largely removing the incentives for tree planting in the area. But the damage had been done, and plans were being hatched in the Scottish Office to bring the NCC under its control.

Although it was the English Secretary of State for the Environment who announced plans to split the NCC in July 1989, it has never been denied that the real architect of the change was the Secretary of State for Scotland and his staff. Arrangements for Wales came almost as an afterthought.

The plan, as announced, was to split the NCC into three country agencies. The Welsh part was to merge with the smaller Welsh section of the Countryside Commission — the body responsible for landscape protection and recreation in the countryside. This would form a new body to look after landscape and wildlife — the Countryside Council for Wales (CCW). The Scottish NCC

was to have a brief independent existence before joining the Countryside Commission for Scotland in April 1992 to form Scottish Natural Heritage (SNH), again with landscape and nature conservation responsibilities. The English NCC was to remain independent as the Nature Conservancy Council for England — although it promptly became known as English Nature (EN). Each agency was to inherit responsibility for its National Nature Reserves, powers to

Above: *Britain's biggest spider, the raft spider is known to exist only on a few vulnerable fens in Suffolk. The country agencies must be endowed with full legislative powers if they are to protect such endangered species.*

Left: *Successful SSSI management depends on cooperation between conservation body and landowner. In this instance, a quarrying company consented to relocate 5.5 hectares of species-rich grassland at the request of English Nature. The new site is now a nature reserve.*

Right: *An NCC report of the 1980s descibed the Flow Country of north-east Scotland as '...the largest single area of habitat in the UK that is of major importance on the world scale because of its global scarcity'. It was largely the NCC's attempts to save the area from afforestation that led to its dissolution in 1991.*

protect Sites of Special Scientific Interest, and all the other responsibilities that had previously rested with the national body.

What these proposals overlooked was the need for a wider overview of nature conservation in Britain or a national perspective on the UK's responsibilities within the European Community and a number of international conservation conventions. Also, there seemed to be no mechanism to decide the allocation of scarce resources. Who would choose between protecting the wildlife of an English chalk down, a Welsh oakwood or a Scottish mountain top?

Eventually the government agreed to an organization to fulfil a global role. However, to ensure that it would not challenge the independence of the new agencies, it was set up as a joint committee of the three country councils. It was called the Joint Nature Conservation Committee (JNCC).

It is still too early to assess the merits or otherwise of the new arrangements. There is no doubt, however, that well over a year of conservation effort has been lost as staff have struggled with revised responsibilities. Also, as each agency develops its own individual methods of working, the job for the British voluntary conservation bodies is becoming more difficult. Organizations like the Royal Society for the Protection of Birds and the British Trust for Ornithology are involved in the conservation and study of birds across Britain, but they now have to liaise separately with all agencies.

The existence of the JNCC has helped to some extent, but it too has had a difficult first year, beset by staff shortages and major administrative problems. Its relationship with the three country agencies also has been distinctly uneasy.

The biggest fear of conservationists was that the new agencies would regard the split of the NCC as a slap across the wrists from the government, warning them not to use their powers too strongly to block

profitable development schemes. Already, there are worrying signs that this might be happening. English Nature, for example, has been criticized for signing a deal with a major peat-extraction company, turning a large area of peatland into nature reserves but still allowing peat to be extracted from two-thirds of it, effectively destroying its plant and animal communities.

In Wales, CCW is directing its efforts towards opening up a network of rights of way, an admirable initiative which walkers welcome but which conservationists fear is deflecting resources away from more pressing problems, such as the needs of the plants and animals themselves.

As yet, there is no evidence that the lapwing, cowslip, otter, sea-slug, purple hairstreak butterfly or any of Britain's other wildlife have suffered from these changes to nature conservation in Britain. But there is also no proof that conditions have improved, and people who care for the wildlife and wild places of Britain will continue to keep a weather eye on the emerging roles of the new conservation agencies.

Michael Scott

*Below: **Looking to the future, teamwork is clearly the best way forward. In a current project to secure feeding and nesting sites for the rare chough, the JNCC coordinates operations across Europe, while the local SNH and the World Wide Fund for Nature provide money.***

RAINBOW WARRIORS

Above: *Greenpeace protesters board a Polaris submarine at the Faslane base near Glasgow to draw attention to its cracked nuclear reactor.*

Far right: *The new Rainbow Warrior was launched four years after the bombing of its predecessor.*

Below: *The Greenpeace base in Antarctica (now dismantled) played a vital role in the fight to preserve the continent.*

Under a threateningly grey sky, a buzzing swarm of Zodiac inflatables scud over the choppy sea, their yellow radiation warning flags flapping bravely in the breeze. As the first Polaris submarine looms into view, the tension in the boats becomes almost palpable as the crews prepare themselves for the confrontation ahead.

In perfect unison, the Zodiacs break ranks and begin darting around the docks as navy-clad sailors look on. Suddenly, one of the inflatables heads straight towards the smooth flank of a sub. As the small craft lunges on to the berthed hulk, two of the crew leap aboard and unfurl a black-and-white banner. The image is stark and needs no explanation. As the banner's ragged white line splits the expanse of black steel, the graphic representation of the submarine's cracked nuclear reactor is clear for all the world's media to see.

Within minutes the coup is complete. But the message endures. Once again a threat to the environment has been confronted directly, confronted by arguably the most dynamic of all the environmental pressure groups: Greenpeace.

Whether driving their tiny boats between a great whale and the explosive harpoon of a Japanese whaler, or blocking the polluting discharge of a factory outfall pipe, there is no mistaking the Greenpeace style. It is bold. It is confrontational. And it is effective.

Greenpeace has been pursuing its campaign of non-violent direct action ever since 1971, when a group of North American activists sailed the *Phyllis Cormack* into the US atomic test zone off Amchitka, Alaska, to protest against the continued testing of nuclear weapons.

From that characteristically bold beginning, Greenpeace has grown into one of the most potent of pressure groups with over five million supporters drawn from nearly 160 different countries. Yet despite the administrative problems which could accompany such growth, Greenpeace has lost none of its radical, cutting edge. It has preserved this partly by keeping its aims simple and partly by maintaining a very streamlined chain of command.

Today, Greenpeace operates on the same basic premise that it adopted 21 years ago: that determined individuals can alter the actions and purposes of even the overwhelmingly powerful by bearing witness — that is, by drawing attention to an environmental abuse through their unwavering presence, whatever the risk. And by bearing witness, Greenpeace can not only inform the public of a crime against the environment, but can also — if only temporarily — stop the crime itself.

While Greenpeace has remained true to its founding principle, the world it seeks to protect has changed immensely. During the 1970s and early '80s environmental issues were of minority interest. Today, however, they command far more attention. And while this trend is to be welcomed, it

brings with it new responsibilities for environmental pressure groups.

This point is not lost on Peter Melchett, Executive Director of Greenpeace UK: 'Today there are far more journalists and people in government who understand the issues. So in one sense at least the political climate is far tougher now for groups such as Greenpeace. We must be much more professional; we must do more research and take more expert scientific advice, for we know that our arguments will have to stand close scrutiny.'

As well as being scientifically sound, it is also important that Greenpeace gets its message across in a clear and consistent manner. It achieves this by having a surprisingly centralized management structure. All its major campaigns are selected by Greenpeace International, which is run by a five-person board elected by representatives from the 30 or so national offices.

Greenpeace UK campaigns, in common with those run by other national offices, are then taken from this campaign list, the choice being based on the appropriateness of the campaign to the country concerned and the availability of suitable resources.

As an entirely independent organization, Greenpeace's resources are derived almost entirely from its supporters. After years of steady growth, Greenpeace saw an explosive surge in support during 1985 following the bombing of the *Rainbow Warrior* in Auckland, New Zealand, by the French Secret Service, and the trend continued the following year after the Chernobyl disaster. But the main growth in support occurred between 1987 and 1990 as environmental issues increasingly stole the political limelight. By 1992, Greenpeace UK had around 400,000 supporters, making it Britain's second largest environmental pressure group after the RSPB.

Greenpeace began its campaigning at sea, and it still remains closely identified with the protection of the marine environment. But today the issues it tackles are far more wide-ranging. In 1992, the key campaigns run from the UK office included: Atmosphere and Energy, Wildlife, Toxics, Civil Nuclear and Military Nuclear.

Atmosphere and Energy is the newest of the Greenpeace campaigns. As campaigner Charlie Kronick explains, 'It grew out of the campaign against acid rain which was originally aimed chiefly at reducing the emissions from power stations. But as global warming became an issue our dependence on fossil fuels — and in particular their consumption by cars — had to be addressed.

'Cars already produce 15 per cent of global CO_2, yet the world's car population of half a billion is set to double in 20 years. As a result of this growth, the CO_2 emissions in Britain from cars alone would exceed the limits agreed by the British government even if they shut down every coal-fired power station in the country.'

As part of the Atmosphere and Energy campaign, Greenpeace has carried out many direct actions: from hanging banners from giant smokestacks to dangling a massive plug from a hot air balloon over the sulphurous chimneys of a Yorkshire power station. But in some cases — such as the campaign to save sea turtles — direct action is simply not appropriate.

Based in the UK offices, Catherine Barr of Greenpeace International has been working on this campaign for the past two years. There are seven species of sea turtle and all are currently endangered. Despite this, large numbers are still being killed for their shells and meat.

With its special interest in ocean ecology Greenpeace was the obvious group to try to relieve the turtles' desperate plight. But as Catherine points out, 'Knowing that the turtles were in trouble was just the start; the

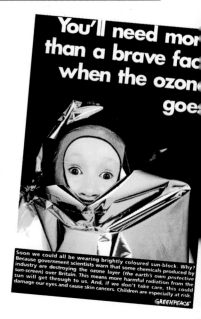

Above: *Following the revelation by NASA scientists that an ozone hole over the Northern Hemisphere could be imminent, Greenpeace stepped up its campaign to publicize the risks to health should this protective layer be destroyed by man-made chemicals such as CFCs.*

Left: *To commemorate the fifth anniversary of the Chernobyl disaster, Greenpeace planted 5000 crosses outside the Soviet-built Bohunice nuclear power plant in Czechoslovakia, as part of their campaign to put pressure on the Czech government to shut it down.*

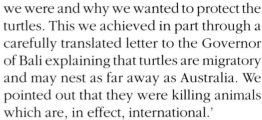

*Right: **Despite being listed on Appendix 1 of the Convention on International Trade in Endangered Species, sea turtles are still being slaughtered.***

*Overleaf: **Preserving Antarctica is regarded as one of Greenpeace's greatest triumphs.***

*Far right: **The use of cars is the most polluting activity on the planet and with a new car produced each second, the number of cars is growing faster than the human population.***

*Below: **Greenpeace campaigners on Sugar Loaf Mountain express their feelings about the Rio Conference, their banner dwarfing that of fellow protestors Climb for the Earth.***

next step was to identify which areas of the world needed most attention.

'Japan proved to be the main market driving the trade and Indonesia the country where more sea turtles are taken than anywhere else, with around 70,000 green and hawksbill turtles being killed every year.'

With no Indonesian office, it was vital that the Greenpeace International campaigners adopt a softly-softly approach and work closely with the local people and conservation groups. 'One of the first tasks facing us was to learn how Balinese law works', explains Catherine.

'It was also crucial for us to explain who we were and why we wanted to protect the turtles. This we achieved in part through a carefully translated letter to the Governor of Bali explaining that turtles are migratory and may nest as far away as Australia. We pointed out that they were killing animals which are, in effect, international.'

The main thrust of the campaign which followed was aimed at tourists going to Bali. Tour operators, airlines, travel agents, hotels and the media were all informed of the turtles' plight and urged to support a ban on the trade in sea turtle products.

This measured approach paid off. After further meetings with the Governor, legislation was drafted which will ban the killing of hawksbill turtles in Indonesia. Proposals have also been put forward to reduce the number of green turtles killed from 20,000 to 3000 over the next few years.

Species-specific campaigns are useful as a focus but it is dangerous to view them in isolation, as everything in the real world is linked. Campaigns to protect the seas or the rainforests not only make more sense from an ecological point of view, but they also allow Greenpeace to maximize its resources. No one appreciates this better than Peter Melchett, who comments: 'In the future we will probably do fewer campaigns but put more resources into them. We will also strive to set clearer goals and present clearer messages, because at the end of the day, we survive on public support. We have to do and say things that mean something to people of many different countries and cultures. Politicians don't listen to what we say because it's clever, or because we have a fleet of ships, but because we have 5 million supporters.'

Despite their diversity, Greenpeace supporters can be broadly characterized: most are under 40 years old and display a more passionate commitment to Greenpeace itself than is typical of the supporters of many other pressure groups. This fervour perhaps reflects the tremendous strength of spirit possessed by the organization itself. For despite the depressing nature of the many challenges faced by Greenpeace, the optimism and commitment within the organization is overwhelming — and contagious. As Peter Melchett says, 'I am only interested in winning campaigns. And although it has been suggested that as we have grown bigger we have become less radical, less effective — the reality is that

today Greenpeace does far more direct actions, on far more issues, in far more countries against far more powerful opponents than we ever did in the early days.'

In 1992, after 21 years of campaigning, Greenpeace scored a particularly symbolic victory. In the spirit of the crew of the *Phyllis Cormack*, which challenged the American nuclear test programme in the North Pacific, Greenpeace campaigners aboard the new *Rainbow Warrior* confronted the French in the South Pacific. As a result of this brave, defiant, non-violent action, the French government was finally persuaded to introduce a moratorium on nuclear weapons testing, bringing us all one step closer to a green and peaceful world.

John Birdsall

NOT ALL DOOM AND GLOOM

Greenpeace has focused the world's attention on many of the most shocking environmental atrocities, and, not surprisingly, the green message often appears to be a depressingly dark one. But throughout its 21-year history, Greenpeace has won an impressive number of victories and it is upon these past successes that hope for the future rests.

● *Following a protest at the test site at Amchitka, Alaska, in 1972, the US nuclear testing programme was abandoned after one explosion.*

● *A worldwide campaign which drew attention to the brutal slaughter of seal pups for their skins led in 1982 to a European Community ban on the import of seal skins.*

● *Intensive lobbying proved instrumental in the ban in 1983 on the dumping of radioactive waste at sea.*

● *The 'Save the Whale' campaign finally achieved a major success when the International Whaling Commission banned commercial whaling in 1986.*

● *Following a campaign against the incineration of toxic wastes at sea, a global ban was enacted in 1988.*

● *In 1990 the North Sea Ministers Conference endorsed a wide range of measures to clean up the North Sea. The UK government also agreed to end waste dumping by 1993 and sewage dumping by 1998.*

● *In 1991, after lobbying of the Antarctic Treaty nations, a 50-year ban on mineral extraction in Antarctica was passed.*

● *After a six-year campaign, Japan announced that by the end of 1992 it would cease large-scale drift netting. The EC also announced a similar ban.*

THE COMMUNICATORS
& EDUCATORS

It is easy to take our interest in and knowledge of the world's animals for granted. Yet it was not so long ago that people viewed the great outdoors and its inhabitants with indifference or hostility. It took visionary and incredibly courageous individuals to move the study of wildlife away from the cramped confines of zoos and museums and out into natural habitats. Just as importantly, it was their skill in communicating their findings that captured the public imagination and turned many of us into amateur natural historians.

Today, the descendants of these first popular naturalists continue to spread the wildlife word, from sound recordist Jeremy West to TV personality and writer Gerald Durrell. We salute the pioneers of natural history, then go back to the future with the high-tech specialists making discoveries in the field today.

It would be difficult to think of a more 'hands-on' experience of wildlife than the work of an African game warden, and the section concludes with a profile of Richard Barnwell, who worked as a warden in Nigeria for nine years.

BEHIND THE MICROPHONE OF A…
WILDLIFE SOUND RECORDIST

Above: *For Jeremy West, sound is like a colourful brush stroke that enriches and brings life to his perception of the environment.*

Right: *Stealthy recording in the reedbeds of Botswana rewarded Jeremy with the unforgettable sound of frolicking hippos.*

One of the great things about wildlife sound recording is that it requires only a small investment in equipment. As a minimum, you need a portable tape recorder, a parabolic reflector, a microphone and a set of headphones — and this is just how I started. I have always enjoyed travelling in remote places in all parts of the world, and had planned an overland drive to Spain, to go walking in the Sierra Nevada mountains. I took a portable cassette recorder quite by chance, and was fascinated by the sounds I heard along the way: cuckoos, nightingales, a ploughman's commands to his mule, donkeys braying, goats' bells, and the richly varied sounds of mountain streams. The quality of these first recordings left a lot to be desired, but it did inspire me to learn more. I took advice from Richard Margoschis of the Wildlife Sound Recording Society (WSRS) during one of his weekend wildlife sound recording courses. I upgraded from cassette to quarter-inch tape, bought some second-hand equipment and built a four-track studio in my home in London, all for surprisingly little expense.

Then the adventure began. For the first two years, I recorded anything I could, from wildlife to music, speech to machinery, raindrops to campfire cracklings. All the time I was discussing my recordings with anyone even remotely involved in sound in order to find the best ways to sell my material. I knew I wanted to take sound recording seriously, and to go professional.

Today I make the main part of my living by recording soundtrack for film, especially for adventure documentaries. One expedition took me to the coast of northern

162
162

morning we drove out to get a radio fix on the tagged animals, and a pulse signal from one of them showed he was within range — about 8km away. The pulse grew louder as we approached downwind to within 60m of him. I could not see our quarry in the long grass but was told that he had been taking a late morning nap. Unexpectedly, he decided to get up and stroll in our direction. Rhinos have acute hearing, but the strong wind blowing towards us concealed our presence. We crouched as best we could in the thick, low bush cover and waited. The sleepy animal was only 12m away when suddenly he spotted us. His forelegs went rigid. Then he turned and bolted, crashing away through the bush in obvious alarm. However, I did capture the sound of the snort and the thundering of heavy feet receding into the distance.

Above: *Four large aluminium suitcases hold all the equipment Jeremy needs on a film recording expedition.*

Chile, by the Atacama Desert, to search for rare cacti. We heard a tremendous amount of activity going on in three large, gnarled trees on the slopes of a gully. When I looked more closely, I saw between 15 and 20 giant hummingbirds zooming around the branches, alternately sucking nectar and snapping up insects, all the time emitting their plaintive whistles. It was a wonderful sight, and good recording too. It was also remarkable in that these are generally solitary birds. I made many other journeys in Chile, always armed with my recorder.

The word 'safari' is Swahili for a journey, and this truly describes every trip you make in Kenya, where I had worked as a bush pilot in the 1970s. I was contacted by an old friend, Dr Robert Brett, who was running a research project on black rhinos on the Laikipia ranch in northern Kenya. He invited me over to record some noises: it seems that rhinos snore very loudly in their sleep. His research area contained about 40 animals, of which two young males had been radio-tagged. Early one very windy

Right: *Working from the cockpit of a light aircraft gave Jeremy access to the rich sights and sounds of rural Africa.*

My choice of equipment depends on the nature of each trip. A top-of-the-line sound studio will contain multi-track recorders, many microphones, electronic sound effect sources, and a mixing console. When I am working in the field, I carry lightweight equipment of equal quality. Typically, this consists of a quarter-inch recorder or a digital audio tape (DAT) recorder, headphones, and either a gun microphone or a parabolic reflector, both of which are ideal for picking up distant sounds. For film work, I include four more microphones, a mini-mixer, a boom, connectors and cables, spare batteries and tapes, a tool kit and repair kit, spare headphones, microphone wind shields, back-up power units, microphone stands, and battery-chargers.

Recording soundtrack for film presents its own particular challenges. I want to

Left: *The high-pitched whistle of the African woodland kingfisher is one of many bird calls in Jeremy's extensive tape archives.*

place my microphone as close as possible to the subject, but the camera takes precedence and I must stay clear of shot. With adventure documentaries in particular there is often no time to discuss the shot in advance, as it all happens so quickly. I must accurately judge the edge of frame and quickly place my microphone just outside it. I switch on my recorder whenever the camera is running: this is known as synchronized sound. Each location also has its own unique ambient sound, and after recording in a location, I ask everyone to be quiet and record for at least 30 seconds. This ambient sound is particularly important when filming dialogue, where it is used to make breaks between sentences and to lead in and out of speech. Any other sound simply would not match the original.

To add atmosphere to the synchronized soundtrack, I also record a lot of what is known as 'wild-track'. A good example of wild-track recording occurred recently while filming in the Okavango Delta for Channel Four's series *The Fragile Earth*. We

Right: *For many hunting mammals, calling can be a means of warning rivals or terrifying prey, and few sounds are more blood-curdling than the roar of a hunting lion.*

Below: *In pursuit of gently snoring rhinos, Jeremy ended up instead with a tape conveying all the excitement of a big male hurtling through the dry Kenyan bush.*

filmed all over the Delta, from light aircraft, Land Rovers, boats and dugout canoes, in the water and out of the water. I put on the wild-track the general ambience as well as the specific calls of the boubou shrike, the yellow-billed kite, the woodland kingfisher and Heuglin's robin. I also recorded canoes gliding through reeds, the sounds of village life, finger pianos and other musical instruments, girls singing, thunder and rain.

I like to house the original recordings of interesting wild-track in my archives, which also hold most of my personal material — from the early work on cassette to new DAT material. I also send sounds to the WSRS for inclusion in their circulating tapes, which

before and after insecticide spraying — but these measurements can be hard to interpret. We know the sound patterns of the tsetse fly, but cannot tell how many other insects produce similar sounds. Nor do we know which of these other insects may also have been affected by the spraying.

Such scientific studies open a number of intriguing questions. For instance, does each habitat have a unique sound spectrum, a sonic 'fingerprint'? Answering this question may tell us whether migrating birds use sound to detect their home area as well as depending on other clues. Another question concerns the degree to which animals compete with each other to be heard. Do species that communicate by sound need to find a space in the ambient noise to avoid clashing with another animal using the same frequency?

A first-hand involvement with wildlife sound recording has introduced me to a remarkably rich and exotic world, and to live without the ability to hear must be very hard indeed. Views of wilderness areas are breathtaking to behold, but the natural symphony of sound brings those wonderful images to life.

Jeremy West

contain fascinating material contributed by members, most of whom are amateurs. Other material from my archives appears in radio programmes and audio-visual soundtracks. My archives give me much pleasure; like a photograph album, they can be dipped into and enjoyed at any time.

Sound recording has become a vital tool for scientists who require a detailed breakdown of the volume of frequencies of the ambient sounds heard in any one place. In the Okavango Delta, the Tsetse Fly Control Organization asked me if they could use sound to assess the effects of their fly eradication programme. The idea is to measure the ambient sounds in the target areas

Left: *Jeremy's senses are sharpened with each successive year of his career. More than ever he notices the everyday sounds around him, such as the screaming of swifts in London's skies, or the crooning call of the fulmar high on the Cornish cliffs.*

AN INTERVIEW WITH...
GERALD DURRELL

Above: *'I get floods of people saying what an influence reading my books has been on them. It's very flattering, and if it's true it's what I always wanted to do with my life.'*

Right: *The black and white ruffed lemur, threatened by habitat destruction in its native Madagascar, is one of many species bred in Jersey.*

Let's make one thing clear, right away, for those who haven't read Gerald Durrell's books or seen him on television. The man doesn't just like animals, he loves them. And he is quite unashamed to admit it.

'Every time I see an animal I think, now that's the animal for me! If I see a giraffe I say, "How marvellous, how wonderful, seeing that lovely female giraffe I wish I were a male giraffe. That long neck, those long legs, just like an American film star."

'Then I see a babirusa (a wild pig from Indonesia with an impressive set of tusks), and I think, "Isn't that absolutely the most marvellous thing in the world!" Though I admit I wouldn't want to kiss one. Then I see a chimpanzee or a gorilla; and there's my wife — she's a primate too, you know.'

Some zoo directors or conservationists may find this attitude embarrassingly unscientific. But the founder and honorary director of the Jersey Wildlife Preservation Trust is not your average zoo director or conservationist. Nor does he claim any great scientific knowledge. 'My wife, Lee, is more scientifically qualified than I am,' he says. 'I am the most ignorant man I know. But my talent is knowing how to put things together and getting other people to do them... and getting all the credit!'

Gerry wanted his own zoo from the age of about six, an ambition which grew and grew, to the consternation of his friends and relatives. His first trip, to Cameroon in 1950, yielded a collection of 500 creatures which he sold to the London and Paignton zoos. He immortalized the trip in *The Overloaded Ark*, the first of many delightful bestsellers about animals and expeditions.

Soon afterwards, Gerry felt that the time had come to establish a zoo of his own. But he was determined that this would be more than just the fulfilment of his childhood ambition: the zoo would specialize in the breeding of rare animals. First, he had to find a site. He needed a place where they made their own rules, but it had to be a holiday resort for the revenue from visitors to make it viable. So he asked his publisher, Rupert Hart-Davis, if he knew anyone in the Channel Islands. He did.

'This chap met me at the Jersey airport,' recalls Gerry. 'He drove me to two or three properties which were unsuitable, and then brought me to his house, Les Augres Manor, for lunch. As we were walking around I said, "This is just what I want". It turned out that he wanted to return to England. So I rented it at first, and bought it later, in 1959.'

The rest, as they say, is history. More than three decades later, the Jersey Zoological Park, or the Jersey Wildlife Preservation Trust, as it came to be called, is recognized as one of the best zoos in the world.

When I visited Jersey recently, my taxi driver said that almost every visitor to the island goes there. 'Not quite everybody,' says Gerry, 'but certainly a large proportion of them. The interesting thing is that many of them, from all over the world, come to Jersey specially to see the zoo. That often surprises local people, who don't realize that we are quite so famous.'

But Jersey is much more than a zoo. It is making a remarkable contribution to conservation, not only through its own breeding activities, but also in encouraging similar projects in other countries, through its conservation education programmes, and in establishing a training centre for conservationists and zoo staff from abroad.

The students — and there have been over 300 from about 70 countries — have returned to share their expertise with their local zoos, and to boost captive breeding programmes in their area. Others work for wildlife in different ways. 'Some have now reached very influential positions in government,' Gerry points out, 'which will be very useful for conservation in the future.'

Among Gerry's honours and awards is a diploma from Argentina. It came without explanation, not even a letter or phone call, but appeared to be for his help in establishing the Valdés Peninsula as a wildlife sanctuary. 'I had gone to Patagonia to make a film and found that it was perfect. It's a sort of bottleneck, and all you had to do was put some guards on the neck of the bottle and you would protect the whole place, with its penguins and elephant seals and whales and everything else.'

Bill Conway, director of the Bronx Zoo in New York, visited Jersey in 1992 to attend a conference on captive breeding. 'Bill is one of the most influential zoo directors in the world,' says Gerry, 'and he told me that he first went to Patagonia after reading my book. He fell in love with it too, and he's just secured the money to protect large chunks of it. I was absolutely delighted, as Patagonia is very special to me.'

In Mauritius and its nearby islands, the Trust has participated in a striking success story by saving several species on the brink of extinction. The Mauritius kestrel (once down to about four birds), the pink pigeon and the echo parakeet — all found only on Mauritius — are looking more secure. In the Caribbean, the St Lucia parrot has recovered, and the local people have become thoroughly involved in saving the species. Tamarins in Brazil, lemurs in Madagascar, the Bali starling and the Majorcan midwife toad are among animals that face a brighter future thanks to the Trust's work.

Gerald Durrell believes it is important that all the animals which Jersey collects and breeds remain the property of the

Left: *The Jersey zoo's involvement in a project to save the St Lucia parrot has met with resounding success.*

Below: *Sea lions feature among the attractions of the Valdés Peninsula in South America, an area of wild beauty for which Gerald has a soft spot.*

Right: *Gerald's dedication to animals, their habitats and their conservation stems from his love of wildlife of all shapes and sizes.*

country they hail from, and that the governments concerned should be able to claim their animals back. 'That's very important with some countries,' he says, 'or they may think it's the great white raj coming in again and pinching all their animals.'

There have been one or two failures, of course. 'I hate failing,' remarks Gerry. 'The volcano rabbit is one example, but I'm sure we'll get it right in the end.' Lee and Gerry went to Mexico to collect some of the endangered rabbits, which did well at first but eventually died. 'For some reason we weren't doing the right thing,' he says. 'We treated them as tropical animals, whereas in fact I think they are probably just very hardy rabbits that happen to live at a great height. Perhaps we should have treated them simply as rabbits.'

He adds that every species is different, and you have to find out the special trick of breeding them. And that applies not only to the species, but to individual animals as well. 'You can't just bung a couple of monkeys in a cage and say "Go ahead and breed" because they might take an instant dislike to each other. On the other hand, they might be made for one another.'

He tells me about the Jersey gorillas. 'We have recently lost one of our oldest female gorillas, Nandi, who was deeply in love with Jambo, her mate. And I mean love. She was devoted to him from the moment she set eyes on him. When Nandi died, Jambo went into mourning — quite literally. He refused his food, sat about and behaved quite differently from normal. It was quite extraordinary to watch.'

Enclosures are important, Gerry believes. 'You can't put a squirrel in a six-foot-tall cage. It's an arboreal animal. It needs height.' He has strong views on some other zoos' enclosures. For example, he doesn't much care for London Zoo's elephant and rhino house. 'I took a Dutch zoo director to see it soon after it opened,' remarks Gerry,

'and he said to me, "What is this? Do they think the elephants go up and roost at night?"' Nevertheless, he wants London Zoo to survive its current financial problems: 'It's terribly important that it does.'

There are other aspects of zoos that he dislikes. 'I hate all the plastic trees and so on that American zoos tend to go in for. Some of it's very clever, but it's Disneyland. I was taken around an American zoo which had lots of plastic trees, plastic everything. It was enormous and it was full of birds. I said to the director, "What do you do when you get a sick bird?" He tried to avoid answering me, but I repeated my question. Eventually he said, "We find the simplest way is to shoot them down with a warm hose". Can you believe it? It's monstrous!'

Gerry sometimes finds it a disadvantage being so easily recognizable, particularly at the zoo. 'People who have seen me on television, or have read my books, ask for autographs. And if you sign one, you have to sign them all.' It's not that he doesn't appreciate his fans and admirers, it's just that the attention can sometimes be inconvenient. 'I'm tending to become crepuscular, like a fruit bat or Count Dracula. I creep around at dusk, or at any rate before ten, when the zoo opens, or after five o'clock.'

Gerry himself earns nothing from the zoo or the Trust's work. His only perk is the 'grace and favour' flat in the manor where he and Lee live. 'In the old days, every time I got a new car, the rumour on the island was, "The zoo must be doing well, we see Gerald Durrell's got a new car." It was a difficult thing to live down.'

The zoo is doing well, and its conservation work is benefiting many rare animals — and by example, many thousands more around the world. Gerald Durrell's army of supporters, and the graduates of his training centre, will ensure that it continues to play a leading role in world conservation.
Nigel Sitwell

Below: *Gerald is determined that the Jersey zoo should continue as it is after he has gone. He is clearly proud of its breeding successes, both at home and abroad.*

PIONEERS OF NATURAL HISTORY

The immense public interest in wildlife is an accepted fact of modern society. We need only look at the television listings, glance along the shelves of bookshops or consider the huge membership of environmental organizations to realize how popular the subject has become. It is easy to assume that there has always been a special concern for the natural world, yet this is far from the case. If we return to the early part of the last century we find that natural history was the sole preserve of a small band of dedicated specialists.

This tiny minority consisted chiefly of men who belonged to the wealthier, more leisured sections of the community. These gifted amateurs were frequently regarded by their contemporaries as eccentrics, but their work — overseas exploration, the collection of animal skins and plants, field observations and writings — have formed the basis of our current awareness and understanding of the natural world.

An outstanding figure among these early pioneers was Charles Waterton. Born in 1782, he was the son of a wealthy Yorkshire landowner who also held large plantations in British Guiana (modern Guyana). At the age of 22, Waterton junior travelled out to manage these South American estates, and it was there that he embarked on his private studies of tropical wildlife. Between 1804 and 1824 he made several expeditions into the Amazonian rainforest, collecting hundreds of birds and mammals. On returning to England, Waterton built his own personal natural history museum at his Yorkshire home, Walton Hall.

He also set about converting his Yorkshire estate into the first ever British nature reserve. A high wall erected around the entire park excluded poachers, and gamekeepers were forbidden to shoot any wild predators. Waterfowl and gamebirds were both encouraged, but for their aesthetic value rather than to supply the dinner table. Having established conditions that were highly favourable for wildlife, Waterton devoted himself to observing it. He experimented with prototype hides to enable intimate studies of animal behaviour and built some of the first ever nestboxes to encourage breeding jackdaws and owls. He used the detailed notes he took as the basis for three volumes of natural history essays, published between 1838 and 1857.

These writings testified to Waterton's painstaking observation of birds and mammals in their natural setting. In the early nineteenth century his peers generally studied their subjects indoors, at the museum bench, working exclusively with dead

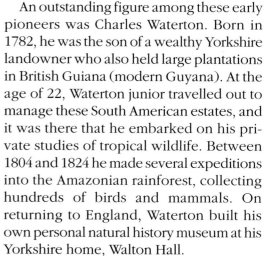

Right: *Alfred Russel Wallace is the lesser known contributor to the theory of evolution. He developed a theory of natural selection independently of Charles Darwin, but was generous in sharing his findings with the other great naturalist.*

Walter Bates (1825–92) and Alfred Russel Wallace (1823–1913). All travelled for long periods in South America, and each later achieved a reputation as a distinguished field naturalist. The first of these, however, went further, for Darwin is undoubtedly the single most important naturalist of the nineteenth century. His book *The Origin of Species* described the very mechanism regulating the living world: the process which we know as natural selection. The image we have inherited of this great scientist is of a heavy-browed, white-bearded sage. Yet in early manhood Darwin was also an adventurous traveller, spending six years on board *HMS Beagle*, which took him to the Cape Verde islands, the Galapagos Islands, Tahiti, New Zealand and Tasmania.

Darwin's account of this journey, *Journal of Researches into the Geology and Natural History of the various Countries visited*

Right: *Audubon's illustrations — here, of a trio of ivory-billed woodpeckers — are remarkable both for their painstaking detail and the vivid way they conjure up a bird's movement.*

skins. Waterton rejected these methods. None of his publications better demonstrates his approach than his immensely popular *Wanderings in South America*.

Published in 1825, the book was an account of his Amazonian journeys, full of exotic tales of his encounters with the natural world. Waterton recalled, for instance, how he had left his toes protruding from his camp bed as a lure for blood-sucking vampire bats, so that he could observe their feeding behaviour at close quarters. He also described an encounter with a large crocodile — a black cayman. He leapt on its back and wrestled it before his servants finally captured the creature. Accounts like these provoked disbelief amongst his peers, yet his book fascinated its nineteenth century audience, and encouraged a generation of younger naturalists to follow in his adventurous footsteps.

Three young men who were inspired by works of natural history like Waterton's were Charles Darwin (1809–1882), Henry

during the Voyage by HMS Beagle, was published in 1839. Its weighty title disguises the most personal and, for the lay-person, most enjoyable of Darwin's publications. Like Waterton's *Wanderings in South America*, it presented natural history as a vibrant process, not just a matter of examining dried bones and pickled skins.

Henry Bates and Alfred Wallace were naturalists and authors in exactly the same mould. However, unlike Waterton or Darwin, they did not inherit a private income. They financed their joint expedition to the Amazonian forests by selling the skins which they collected. Setting out in 1848, Bates and Wallace travelled up the Amazon for almost two years. Eventually the two men parted company, Wallace remaining in South America a further 24 months, while Bates continued for an additional nine years. Bates, a meticulous field naturalist, amassed a huge number of specimens, representing 14,712 species. Of this total, 8000 — most of them insects — were completely new to science. Bates' account of his 11-year expedition, *The Naturalist on the River Amazon*, published in 1863, is a classic work of natural history exploration that remains widely available today.

While Bates' reputation as an author rests on this sole work, Alfred Wallace was a prolific writer on a wide range of subjects. Moreover, his own journeys in tropical regions exceeded even those of his early companion. After his four years in South America, Wallace switched his attention to the rainforests of Southeast Asia. Here he remained for eight years. As a consequence of his studies Wallace developed, independently of Darwin, the idea that all life forms had evolved as a result of the process of natural selection. This momentous theory was first announced at a scientific meeting in 1858, in a paper written by both men.

Wallace remained a staunch supporter of Darwin's ideas about the origins of life, and was one of the most important thinkers on evolution in the nineteenth century. He also wrote more autobiographical works that described his expeditions in the tropics, such as *Travels on the Amazon and Rio Negro* and *The Malay Archipelago*.

However important the scientific papers and books of authors like Wallace, it was not the written word alone which brought the world of nature alive for Victorian society. Improvements in the quality and supply of paper, the development of the

Below: *John James Audubon produced illustrations of great accuracy and quality that left the public clamouring for more.*

Above & right: *'The Ancient Wrasse' from The Aquarium, by Victorian writer and illustrator Philip Henry Gosse. Such works led to a vogue for aquaria.*

Below: *Early naturalists were lampooned by contemporaries as harmless eccentrics, as in this Swedish cartoon of the household of Sir William Buckland.*

steam-powered press and important innovations in colour-printing methods paved the way for an array of gifted wildlife artists to help popularize the subject.

Perhaps the most important of these was John James Audubon, an American born in 1785. As a young man Audubon neglected business and family to devote himself to his wildlife paintings. After a visit to Britain in 1826 to generate financial support for his project, Audubon embarked on his legendary book, *The Birds of America*. Its completion in 1838 was in every sense a colossal achievement. The four volumes each measured 100 x 68cm, and contained 435 plates in total. Illustrating freshly killed birds to obtain the truest colours, and depicting them life-sized or larger, Audubon produced what is probably the most famous collection of bird paintings ever. In 1984 a full set of this magnificent work sold for £1.1 million.

Audubon's art inspired a wide public demand for large-format collections of animal paintings and created a climate in which younger wildlife artists could flourish. One such figure was John Gould. Born in 1804, he was the most important British painter of birds in the nineteenth century, although 'publisher' might more accurately describe Gould's role. The paintings were completed by his wife, Elizabeth, and a team of talented artists including Edward Lear, the writer of nonsense verse. Nonetheless it was Gould who had the business acumen to ensure that his many volumes of colour plates, including his five-volume *The Birds of Europe*, published between 1832 and 1837, and the subsequent seven-volume *Birds of Australia*, found an enthusiastic audience.

In their efforts to stimulate public interest in wildlife paintings, men like Audubon or Gould had a number of advantages, which related to the qualities of their subject — the birds themselves. Highly varied, easily visible, dynamic and often exquisitely beautiful, birds made almost ideal subjects for the artist. Even individuals confined to the written word like Wallace or Bates had the inherent drama of exotic locations to capture the audience's imagination. No such advantages, however, were available to Phillip Henry Gosse. For Gosse, born in 1810, concentrated primarily on marine biology. Many of his animal subjects were visible only with the aid of a microscope.

This might seem unpromising territory for a bestseller, yet Gosse became one of the most popular authors writing on natural history in the mid-Victorian period. While his early works — *The Canadian Naturalist* and *Birds of Jamaica* — focused on the wildlife he had seen during his 12 years across the Atlantic, Gosse's most successful books had titles such as *The Ocean, A Naturalist's Rambles on the Devonshire Coast, Seaside Pleasures, The Aquarium* and *Evenings at the Microscope*. As well as his considerable talents as illustrator and writer, Gosse was also one of the first to discover that aquatic life, from sea anemones to prawns or fish, might be maintained and studied in the home when kept in a glass case. Thanks to his book *A Naturalist's Rambles on the Devonshire Coast*, aquaria became fashionable additions to the drawing rooms of thousands of Victorian homes.

In books such as *The Aquarium*, Gosse used the latest techniques of chromolithography and was one of the first to include colour plates in a work aimed at a mass market. Through his exploration of this new technology, Gosse alerted his Victorian audience to the strange and often beautiful creatures that existed inside a seaside rockpool. This innovation demonstrates a quality that unites all these gifted and extraordinary pioneers. Their efforts awakened an awareness and an understanding of parts of the natural world which had previously been unknown or overlooked. Through their work, they bequeathed us a legacy fundamental to our understanding of the world around us.

Mark Cocker

CHARLES DARWIN

As a child and young man, Charles Darwin showed little indication of his future gifts as a scientist. He was unremarkable at school, unmotivated as a medical student at Edinburgh University and a failure as a trainee clergyman at Cambridge. While he was at

Cambridge, however, Darwin became an avid collector of beetles, and this hobby led to him being invited to travel as a naturalist on board the HMS Beagle *in 1831.*

It was on this five-year voyage that Darwin found his vocation as a naturalist. His detailed observations of wildlife formed the basis of much of his life's work. Near the journey's end, the variations of species he saw on the Galapagos Islands galvanized the insights Darwin had been developing about the evolution of species.

Back in England, however, it was many years before Darwin published his theory of natural selection. In fact it was only in 1858, when Alfred

Russel Wallace was on the verge of publishing his own findings on the same subject, that Darwin was persuaded to present his principles of natural selection to the public. The Origin of Species caused as much controversy as Darwin had feared. By the time he died in 1882, however, 'survival of the fittest' was a widely accepted premise for life on earth, and the eminent scientist was honoured with burial in Westminster Abbey.

SIGNALS FROM THE SEA

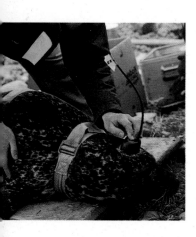

Above: *Satellite telemetry is an effective means of tracking mammals — even far out at sea.*

Far right: *The grey seal is a familiar sight, but how much do we really know about its lifestyle in the wild?*

Right: *The bottle-nose dolphin uses a sophisticated sonar system to track its prey.*

On a sunny day in August 1989 a grey seal surfaced off the Humberside coast to breathe briefly before slipping back into the grey-green depths. Lifting its snout, it exposed the short, rigid antenna glued to its crown. As the water ran off an optical submergence sensor, a micro-controller flashed a message to the Mariner Radar transmitter on the seal's back and a radio signal beamed up through the cloudless sky to one of two orbiting satellites. The message bounced back to the Argos Satellite System base in Toulouse, France, and from there to a back room at the Sea Mammal Research Unit (SMRU) in Cambridgeshire: Seal C has surfaced.

The SMRU is allied to the British Antarctic Survey, part of the National Environment Research Council, and the satellite tracking of three grey seals between 1985 and 1989 was just one of many research projects that it carries out each year. Although the grey seal is relatively common off Britain's coasts, a lack of effective monitoring methods has left much to be discovered about its habits and lifestyle — a fact which became tragically apparent when the common seal population was decimated by the plague of 1988. But sea mammals and many other wild species now have a new and powerful ally — high technology.

At a marine mammal symposium held in London in April 1992, and attended by researchers from Britain, the United States and Canada, Mike Fedak and other SMRU researchers presented their research on grey and common seals. Many of their in-depth studies of marine mammals rely on three separate monitoring systems: satellite-linked data-loggers, ultrasonic acoustic transmitters and VHF radio. These can be used in combination to yield data on diving depth, swimming speed, heart response and other bodily functions. Fedak and SMRU colleague David Thompson conducted just such a field study on grey seals off the Scottish coast in the summer of 1989. Using soluble glue, they fixed data-loggers with VHF and acoustic transmitters to sedated seals; these included pressure transducers and velocity sensors to measure depth and speed. Copper electrodes placed around the heart area monitored the heart rate, which was transmitted on an FM carrier signal. The seals were released within the hour and pursued by the scientists in a power boat. Keel-mounted hydrophones picked up the acoustic FM, speed and depth data from a maximum range of 1km. At greater range, the VHF transmitter gave location fixes and surfacing records.

Results showed that each grey seal travelled between foraging or haul-out sites by diving continuously, and barely swam at all at the surface, where the high drag factor

Right: *Dolphins have little defence against their invisible enemy: the fishing net. Acoustic reflectors may greatly enhance their chances of survival.*

Right: *The spectrogram used in dolphin research is basically a musical score — a graph of pitch against time. With a little simple arithmetic, it can divulge some of the secrets of a dolphin's echo-location methods.*

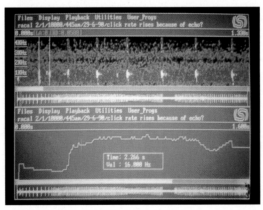

would rapidly exhaust it. Fedak and Thompson established that a seal swims actively on the ascent and descent of a dive but seems to lie in wait for prey at the sea bed, probably as a means of conserving energy. The heartbeat dropped steeply on dives of more than 7–10 minutes' duration, to as low as three or four beats per minute. Other seals, such as Weddell seals, manage long dives by metabolizing without the use

of oxygen, but the grey seal seems simply to reduce its metabolic rate in order to save energy. Conclusions from this and other SMRU tests are interesting not only to scientific bodies but also to conservation organizations eager to understand more about animals at risk: they help to build up a picture of a species' niche within an ecosystem and the threats that may face it.

Studying a threatened species' natural behaviour is a key step towards protecting it — especially when an insight into its habits yields the very means of leading it out of conflict with human activities. David Goodson of Loughborough University's Sonar and Signal Processing Group has spent more than four years on a case of this nature. He is working with Margaret Klinowska of Cambridge University and others, including animal trainer Peter Bloom, to find a way to reduce the number of dolphins and other small cetaceans accidentally trapped during gill-net fishing

lamp. In seawater, the energy peak of each broadband pulse has a wavelength of about 12.5mm, which means that an object must be at least this wide if it is to reflect the click to the dolphin. A smaller object, such as a shrimp or the fibre of a net, simply scatters the signal and is far harder to detect. Large fish present no such problem: the dolphin is an expert hunter of species with a typical length of 30–35cm. Trials suggested that Freddie could detect such prey at a maximum range of about 70m, but the finer details of his fishing technique had to be analyzed back at the lab.

Goodson fed his tapes into an IBM computer which hosted the very latest Texas Instruments digital signal processor (DSP). Displayed on the monitor, the jumbled sounds were represented as a dazzling, multi-coloured spectrogram. The rapid clicks of Freddie's sonar were visible as a track of short white lines, and his breathing

operations. Each year, an estimated 100,000 dolphins worldwide are entangled in twine or mono-filament nets, some of which are up to 50km long. Goodson is convinced that nets can be made acoustically more detectable to these mammals, which use echo-location when hunting in the dim seawater. Between 1989 and 1992 Freddie, a dolphin resident for some time off the Northumberland coast at Amble, gave Goodson the rare chance to observe its use of sonar. The research team placed buoys equipped with underwater hydrophones and radio transmitters in the shallow coastal waters. These 'sonobuoys' picked up the sound of Freddie's sonar clicks and relayed them directly to a four-channel tape recorder back on shore.

As it hunts, a bottle-nose dolphin produces a stream of clicking noises. Each click holds a broad spectrum of frequencies, with the higher frequencies focused forwards into a beam rather like that of a miner's

Left: Peter Bloom's wide knowledge of dolphins' habits has proved invaluable to the research project. He is seen here holding a hydrophone boom in dolphinarium trials, where the mammals' echo-location techniques were explored. David Goodson films from the roof.

Above: *The streamlining and miniaturization of radar enables wildlife researchers to follow their subject in almost any environment.*

Above right: *A rare view of a diving elephant seal in full data-logging kit.*

Right: *Tagging tests on migrating sea turtles help scientists to identify their breeding beaches, many of which are abused by the tourist industry.*

cycle showed up in primrose smudges. The DSP computed the time interval between each click pair, and the original vocal track confirmed the theory — now widely accepted — that a dolphin varies its click rate as a response to the range of its prey. As Freddie searched for prey he emitted an irregular click pattern, but when he 'locked on' to a fish the clicks soon kept a perfectly regular beat. As he closed in on the target, the clicks soared into a high-pitched mewing sound before the final capture. The team could calculate not only Freddie's detection range, but also his speed of approach relative to the fish.

This information led to the next stage of research. While a dolphin is locked on to a fish, its ability to detect echoes from other objects is impaired — although the fact that it has never been seen to crash into rocks or a pier suggests that it has some idea of its environment. But problems arise when an unexpected obstacle — such as a net — lies in its path. The dolphin cannot piece together all the tiny ghost 'glints' bouncing from the mesh, and a collision is likely. When after a fish swimming beyond the

net, the mammal is in even greater peril. Goodson's solution was this: to present the dolphin with a mass of acoustic signals each slightly stronger than a typical prey signal, in order to create the clear image of a wall. In the labs the team tested several reflectors, ranging from tiny aluminium prismatic spheres and 7cm steel balls to ovoid, air-filled plastic designs. It was now time to put these 'cat's eyes' to the test.

Late in 1991, Goodson and Klinowska set up a trial in Scotland's Moray Firth, where a school of dolphins regularly swam past the coast. The team tethered a buoyed rope line at a right angle to the coast, and from this they suspended weighted ropes at 2m intervals along a 100m section. Prototype acoustic reflectors were fixed, again at 2m intervals, to each rope. Cliff-top observers used an electronic theodolite to log the dolphins' course as they surfaced to breathe. A sonobuoy hydrophone was deployed near the rope line to radio acoustic information to the four-channel recorder.

On the third day of tests a group of dolphins approached the rope, close to the coastline. They detected the rope at a range of 150–170m. After a pause in which they hammered the obstacle with sonar clicks, they all turned and skirted it, then sampled the line from behind before swimming off. All the dolphins, that is, except one, which appeared not to detect the rope line until

it was some 20m distant. It apparently came in 'blind', using its sonar only when alerted by the noises of its companions. It retreated rapidly before safely rejoining the others, but, had the obstacle been a net, the straggler may well have met with disaster.

Although the results of this single series of tests have vindicated many of the team's hypotheses, they leave important questions unanswered, particularly in the nature of the reflector. A 5cm prismatic sphere gives a good acoustic glint, but it will be difficult to rig to a net in large numbers. Fishermen will prefer the smooth lines of the plastic ovoid, but will it deter a dolphin? Additional tests, and the funds with which to conduct them, are needed before these ideas can become a life-saving reality.

The enterprising ventures of individuals such as Goodson and Klinowska are just as important as big-budget research programmes. For they both demonstrate that technology can, when properly used, help us piece together the infinitely complex jigsaw that is the natural world and so enhance our efforts to preserve it.

Matthew Turner

GREEN GOLFING WITH BLUWATER

No field of scientific research is complete without its odd-balls, and the story of the biodegradable golf ball makes for one of the oddest stories of all. Any visitor to the seaside is likely to notice the messy tide of man-made rubbish borne in by the tide. An ugly sight, this form of pollution also presents a very real threat to wildlife. In 1990 MARPOL, the world maritime legislative body, banned the dumping of plastic refuse into the world's oceans, following the discovery of bags and other plastic products in the bodies of whales, turtles, dolphins and other marine animals. All cruise ships consequently disallowed the highly popular pastime of driving golf balls from their stern decks — but the golfers were not to be outdone.

An inventive employee of Bluwater Golf Products in San Diego, California, has designed and patented an all-organic, water-soluble ball that travels up to 170m when hit. The core is a blend of sodium citrate and sodium bicarbonate. Covering this is a bonded mixture of paper pulp, seaweed or gelatin. This product has reopened oceanic golf to nearly 200 ocean liners, thousands of offshore drilling platforms and countless waterfront driving ranges. In the interest of ocean animals everywhere, Dr James Nelson of Bluwater Golf is closely monitoring the dissolution characteristics, smell, taste and digestibility of the new 'Aquaflyte'. He is even channelling profits from the sale of the eco-ball into the Bluwater Environmental Foundation. This project, headed by Nelson, offers financial incentives to groups who devise other practical means of greening marine recreational activities.

AFRICAN WILDLIFE WARDEN

Above: *Richard Barnwell has spent much of his working life in Nigeria, where local people hold him in very high esteem.*

Far right: *The leopard is in its element in the Gashaka Gumpti Reserve, where prey animals are abundant.*

Right: *The Defassa waterbuck has an oily coat to help it cope with its wet habitat.*

For many, the term 'game warden' conjures up an image of a military figure pacing the perimeter of a fenced reserve. The reality is very different. I caught a true glimpse of a warden's life when I talked to Richard Barnwell, who has devoted his career to conserving wildlife. He spent nine years as a game warden in Nigeria and now coordinates the work of conservation projects from the headquarters of the World Wide Fund for Nature (WWF) in Surrey.

Richard's fascination with the outdoors dates back to his childhood in East Africa. One of his earliest memories is of crossing the Serengeti in 1954, when only a single-track road meandered across the endless plains and six lonely huts were the sole sign of human habitation. It was these haunting images of an Africa teeming with wildlife, and relatively undiscovered by today's standards, that spurred Richard towards a career in conservation.

Although governments took an increasing interest in 'green issues' in the 1970s, ecology was still an unusual career choice at the time and Richard completed one of only two ecological science degrees then available. After leaving university he began work in Nigeria, starting an association with the country that was to last many years.

His task was to set up the Gashaka Gumpti Reserve, which lies in one of the most remote regions of Nigeria, near the border with Cameroon.

The variety of species it contains makes Gashaka an exciting reserve. Today, troops of up to 50 mona monkeys bound noisily along the branches. At least seven other primate species thrive there, including the Ethiopian colobus monkey, anubis baboon and white-nosed monkey. The lush forests also conceal some magnificent cats, including the leopard and the golden cat, one of the rarest of the small cats. Grazing herds of antelope, hartebeest and many gazelle species often stray from the plains into the forests. The more remote uplands of the reserve are as yet unexplored, and the WWF hope that they may even find mountain gorillas lurking there.

Before Gashaka Gumpti was established, a series of meetings took place between representatives from the Nigerian government, local government and the nearby villages. The boundaries of the reserve were first agreed on paper, and then local employees marked out the area with stone cairns and steel signs. The game guards also set about clearing a 5m strip of vegetation to act as a buffer zone around the boundary of the reserve.

Richard learnt the language so that he could explain to local people the reasons for conservation work and the benefits of living within a conservation area. One of his first tasks was to employ villagers to build roads across the reserve, with access monitored at a single entry point.

It was hoped that if poaching were fully eradicated in Gashaka, animals such as Derby's giant eland (a subspecies of the giant eland) might be enticed to cross the Cameroon border and return to their old haunts. The new roads also allowed game guards to move swiftly through the reserve in pursuit of poachers, and enabled local people to transport produce for the first time to sell in neighbouring villages.

Although planning for local people is commonplace in the '90s, the establishment of Gashaka represented a new approach. Richard explains the shift in attitude. 'In the 1950s game wardens concentrated on policing the reserves but today a greater emphasis is placed on maintaining a good rapport with local people.'

He has fond memories of his time in Gashaka. 'The seven years in Nigeria were the most challenging of my career. It was a real pioneering job going out into an area where very little development had taken place and lifestyles hadn't changed for centuries. Relating to people from a twentieth-century vantage point involved crossing an enormous cultural bridge.'

For Richard, this meant being accepted by a population whose beliefs were largely animist. 'There is a whole spirit world out there which we have no insight into. For them it's a very real world — even the most mentally well-put-together person will talk to you very seriously about the spirits.'

When Richard chose a secluded patch of forest in which to build his home, the local people warned him that a village had once occupied the site. As the dead were usually buried in back gardens the site was thought to be full of spirits. Despite the warnings,

Below: *Hippopotamuses are widespread in central Africa. They spend the day resting in the shallows of rivers.*

Left: *Richard believes emphatically that a conservation project manager must be prepared to work in the field with the staff.*

he went ahead and built the house. He discovered that this was interpreted as an extraordinary ease with the spirit world, and stories circulated that he actually talked to the spirits. When a number of notorious poachers coincidentally died in accidents, Richard assumed supernatural powers in the eyes of the locals and became known as the 'man with magic'.

Although poachers are clearly a menace, there is often a need for wardens to kill animals within the reserve. This may appear to be at odds with the aims of conservation, but reserves are often so successful that animal numbers escalate and must be controlled. 'At Gashaka baboons and monkeys were trampling the crops of local farmers. To let the farmers destroy the animals themselves would have been shirking my responsibility,' Richard explains.

The current generation of wildlife project managers have had their role widened to include research work and the training of local staff. Many game wardens, such as those working in Tanzania, spend much of their time attending government meetings, where they put their case for the preservation of national parks. In Nigeria, Richard devoted much of his time to patrolling with the game guards.

'There can be a tendency for the senior officer to stay in the office while the game guards patrol a reserve,' he recalls. 'This method never works and I feel that you must have people who will go out in the field: it immediately boosts morale.' He believes that leadership is the key to success. 'A passionate commitment to conservation projects is not enough: you must be adaptable. It's no use having people that are so obsessed with what they do that they fall apart at the first hurdle.'

For Richard and other workers at WWF, enduring the political upheavals of countries such as Ethiopia is both frustrating and disappointing. 'Until the war in the north of the country stopped it was pointless,' he says. 'All we were doing was allowing the Ethiopian government to divert more funds into fighting a ridiculous war.'

Above: *The secretary bird is a peculiarly long-legged bird of prey that kills and eats snakes.*

Right: *The needs of migratory animals such as wildebeest present a special challenge to a game park, with its artificial boundaries.*

Below: *Buffalo thrive so well in Gashaka that game wardens must often cull a few in order to control numbers.*

While working on a farming project with the WWF in Somalia, the Barnwell family found themselves living in a police state as the civil war escalated. 'Many of the roads were mined and avoiding being blown up became a daily task. Each day you heard of someone falling victim to a road mine.' Months of planning and hard work were undone in a bombing raid by the Somali airforce. The planes flattened a dam that Richard's conservation project had been building to contain water for irrigation.

Despite these setbacks, Richard has always persevered to ensure that his conservation projects are a success. In Ethiopia he worked on a project funded by the European Community to improve peasant

conservation projects and drawing up new plans. These proposals must be pushed through government committees if they are to receive funds. Although he spends much of his time on paperwork, visits to the field to advise at ground level are also essential.

He hopes that Gashaka will become as big an attraction as Cameroon's Korup National Park. One of the few parks to combine forest and savannah, Gashaka offers many options for tourists. They can sample the sights of the rainforest on foot or ride in jeeps through open grasslands. Richard is enthusiastic: 'We are rebuilding the infrastructure, retraining the staff, and education and conservation programmes are underway for all the villages — education will be the major thrust of the new phase.'

In Gashaka, a school is usually little more than a hut, and a blackboard may be the only teaching aid available. The WWF aims to improve conditions and to provide educational materials which focus on local conservation projects. It is all part of the new initiatives that Richard has seen in his time working in the field, helping humans and wildlife to live in harmony with each other.

Suzanne Jones

agriculture. 'We imported over 150,000 tonnes of fertilizer each year. Farmers knew that using it would improve their yields and were using it almost continuously.'

This source of aid actually did more harm than good. 'The farmers were becoming trapped in a cycle of fertilizer dependency', he explains. 'No other work was being done on green manuring or crop rotation, or on teaching them how to use their own resources. All their hopes were pinned on buying fertilizer, and when the money ran out they were going to be left high and dry.'

Richard's latest role at WWF headquarters has taken him back to Gashaka. He now coordinates projects in Africa, dividing his time between reporting on existing

Left: *Baboons form close-knit communities in the forests. They have a tendency to raid crop fields, however, and game wardens must manage them attentively.*

THE GREEN PAGES

Every day exciting discoveries are made about

many species, but new threats also arise with alarming frequency.

To help keep you abreast of these changes, the Green Pages include

updates of many of the key features in the 1992 Yearbook, together

with a calendar of the year's environmental events.

For anyone keen to find out more about the issues

covered in this year's book, there is a comprehensive book list, and

for those seeking a more creative involvement there are details of

natural history competitions run each year. There is also a table of

the major environmental organizations listing the kind of

volunteer help they require.

Sadly, words such as 'endangered' and 'rare' are

increasingly used to describe many of the world's species.

In a special feature we define these terms and list some of the

animals affected. Finally, there is a useful directory of international

and British wildlife and conservation organizations.

Left: The brimstone butterfly
is widely distributed in England, Wales and
parts of Ireland. Its range reflects the
abundance of the buckthorn and alder
buckthorn plants on which the adult and the
caterpillar respectively feed.

UPDATE ON '92

NEW LEASE OF LIFE FOR PANDAS

In January 1992, after two years discussing an ambitious World Wide Fund for Nature (WWF) plan to add a further 14 reserves for the giant panda, the Chinese government promised more than £1 million to establish the first four reserves. This is an important step as the captive breeding programme carried out in the 1980s had lost its momentum. Ironically, however, after producing only one short-lived panda in 10 years, the Wolong Centre produced twins in September 1991. The money pledged by the Chinese government will also go to fund schemes to encourage the forestry industry to stop logging in the reserve areas and to encourage local villagers to carry out sustainable agriculture outside the reserves.

WWF are, in the long term, looking for an investment of nearer £50 million to fund the entire project.

CONDORS FLYING FREE

After five years in which no California condors flew over the mountains of southern California, these magnificent birds of prey can once again be seen in their natural habitat. In 1987 the last of the wild condors was captured in an attempt to save the bird from extinction. Scientists had pinned all their hopes on a controversial captive breeding programme. Thankfully, by the end of 1991 numbers in the zoos involved had risen from 27 to 51 and a careful reintroduction to the wild was possible. Two eight-month-old birds were released in mid-January 1992 and are reported to be doing well. It is hoped that captive-bred condors will continue to be successfully released until at least two separate wild populations exist, each consisting of a hundred birds.

KING CHEETAH FOUND

The king cheetah is a handsome and extremely rare variant of the common cheetah with a dramatic black-and-gold, leopard-like coat. The only sightings of this big cat had been in southern Africa until recently, when a skin was recovered from a poacher from Burkina-Faso in west Africa.

NEW SPECIES COME TO LIGHT

A number of new animals appear to have been discovered following the exploration of the remote Vu Quang nature reserve in western Vietnam. During a survey organized by the WWF and the Vietnamese Forestry Ministry, a large dagger-horned, goat-like mammal, several fish, a sunbird and a new race of yellow box tortoise were found. The discovery of the 'goat' is particularly exciting, since few large mammals have been discovered this century.

GIANT CLAMS SAVED

Operation Clamsaver, a project based at Orpheus Island in Queensland, Australia, has been a huge success. Eight Pacific nations took part in the project to conserve several species of giant clam. After only seven years, however, the researchers found they had reared over 90,000 clams and had to ask the navy to help move the huge bivalves to suitable reintroduction sites. The clams were transported to their new homes in children's paddling pools on the decks of the ships.

EUROPEAN AGREEMENT ON BATS

On the 4th December 1991 an agreement on the conservation of bats in Europe was signed under the Bonn Convention. The agreement is designed to help conserve a network of safe roosts and feeding sites for all 30 species of European bat, many of which have declined dramatically in recent years. In the autumn of 1991 the mouse-eared bat was officially declared extinct in Britain — a single male had been hanging on in one site in southern Britain but failed to make an appearance in 1991.

NORTH SEA DOLPHINS TOO...

A new agreement under the Bonn Convention was signed by Britain in May 1992 to help promote the conservation of small cetaceans — dolphins and porpoises — in the North Sea. The main threats to these sea mammals appear to come from pollution, disease and accidental entrapment in fishing nets. One of the first tasks undertaken as a result of the agreement will be an attempt to collate more comprehensive information about cetacean populations. This will lead to suggestions about how their conservation can best be approached.

BRITISH BIRDS DECLINE

According to surveys by the British Trust for Ornithology, there was a significant fall in the breeding rate of Britain's main bird species during 1991. Breeding numbers of the tawny owl were the lowest since surveys began in 1963. This drop may be the result of a decline in the populations of its prey species — mice, voles and other small mammals. Other bird species suffering the decline included the wren, whitethroat, robin, blackcap, blackbird and song thrush. The chaffinch was the only species for which an increase in breeding rate was recorded. This increase was probably due to a heavy crop of the beech mast which the chaffinch eats.

NEW ATTEMPTS TO SAVE SIBERIAN CRANE

The Indian wintering population of the Siberian crane continues to balance perilously on the brink of extinction. Large numbers of the rare bird are believed to have been shot as they flew north to their summer breeding grounds, and only four Siberian cranes overwintered in India during 1991–1992.

In early 1992 Russian conservationists released 11 captive-bred chicks along the River Ob in the western Siberian plains, part of the crane's migration route. If the Indian population of the Siberian crane becomes extinct in spite of these efforts, then attempts will be made to release a number of captive-bred Siberian cranes into the common crane's breeding grounds. It is then hoped that the birds will be guided back to India when the common cranes migrate.

ENVIRONMENTAL ISSUES

WETLANDS THREAT

The cattle-free status of the great Okavango Delta in Botswana may soon be under threat. Cattle generate both prestige and wealth for local farmers. Already almost half the population is involved in cattle-rearing, and the country has reached its full cattle-carrying capacity. The number of cattle used to be kept in check by disease carried by the tsetse fly, which invaded the region in 1925, but modern methods of fly eradication have opened up the possibility of grazing in the Okavango Delta, one of the world's most important wetland sites. However, conservationists have so far succeeded in persuading the government to keep the Okavango Delta cattle-free. Fear of foot-and-mouth disease spreading from the wild population to domestic animals has led to the erection of a fence which now surrounds the delta to the south and will soon extend up the northern banks of the Okavango River that feeds the delta.

The erection of the fence has led to some unexpected conflicts. As well as controlling disease, the fence serves to keep cattle out of the grazing lands of the delta. Despite the severe drought affecting southern Africa, the water level in the delta is at its highest for 20 years, so cattle farmers are looking with increasing anger at the grazing set aside for wildlife. Local peoples that used to graze cattle in the delta before the advent of the tsetse fly claim that they are being kept out of traditional grazing lands. However, the loss of their cattle has led many people to take up a hunter-gatherer lifestyle. While the vital natural resources on which they depend would be lost if cattle grazing were extended deep into the delta, the fence itself is keeping these people out of many areas on which they depend for food. It is also causing the death of many wild animals by interfering with their traditional migration routes. A government fact-finding team is currently investigating the various arguments. Its findings will almost certainly influence the government's land use and development plan for the Okavango.

RHINOS STILL THREATENED

Despite hopes in recent years that the trade in rhinoceros horns from Africa had been abating, recent reports indicate that there has in fact been a large increase. There are thought to be fewer than 3500 black rhinos left in the wild. One major dagger producer in Yemen, where rhino horns are carved to make ornate handles on the weapons, has recently imported over 750kg of horn believed to have come from at least 260 rhinos. The bulk of the horn appears to come from Zimbabwe, where the government has recently responded by instigating a programme to dehorn its remaining black rhinos in an attempt to deter poachers, the major culprits.

CITES MEETING '92

In March the Convention on International Trade in Endangered Species (CITES) met in Kyoto in Japan. One of the main issues was the global ban on trade in elephant ivory imposed by CITES in 1989. Four South African countries — Botswana, Malawi, Zimbabwe and

Namibia — wanted to allow limited trade of elephant products, including ivory, on the basis that wildlife should pay for its keep. At the Convention, however, overwhelming pressure from other African nations forced these countries to withdraw their proposals. Despite this, the controversy surrounding the 'farming' of wildlife is far from resolved and will remain a major area of disagreement in the future.

Also at the meeting, there were strong campaigns from organizations such as the RSPB to ban the import of wild-caught bird species for the pet trade and, more specifically, the trade in parrots. It was agreed that countries should now keep records of bird deaths in transit and suspend trade in those species which suffer significant mortality. However, there was some argument over the definition of 'significant' in this context and the UK proposed far lower levels than those which the Convention eventually accepted. There were also no clear moves to curtail the overall trade in wild birds. The RSPB is running a campaign to draw attention to those airlines that are still involved in transporting wild-caught birds.

POLLUTION OF WAR – THE GULF

Over a year after the environmental holocaust in Kuwait resulting from the Gulf War, all the burning oil wells have been extinguished but the landscape is still scarred with treacherous oil lakes. Some of these have begun to harden but the centres are still liquid, luring unsuspecting birds and insects to their death. The Gulf is an important flyway for migrating birds, many of which are fatally attracted to these 'lakes', thinking they are water-filled. Resident species of desert bird have been heavily sooted by the smoke from burning wells but it seems that colonies of terns and other seabird species nesting farther south in the Gulf have not been as badly affected as was initially feared.

A longer-term problem is the pollution of the groundwaters in Kuwait: it is estimated that 7.2 billion litres of seawater were used to put out the fires and this depletion could now seriously affect vital freshwater supplies. There are also threats to the sea mammals in the Gulf. Of particular concern is the long-term effects of the oil slicks on the endangered dugong, which feeds on sea-grasses in the shallow waters.

TIGER POACHING CONTINUES

Poachers have sustained their hunting of tigers in the Indian reserve of Ranthambhor, the flagship of the WWF-sponsored recovery operation Project Tiger. Tiger numbers have fallen from 44 to 15 over the last three years, despite a CITES ban on trade in tiger products. The increase in poaching is linked to the growing demand for tiger bone as a medical remedy in Japan, South Korea and Taiwan.

WILDLIFE AND CONSERVATION ORGANIZATIONS

ICELAND LEAVES IWC

In February Iceland gave notice to quit the International Whaling Commission (IWC). It announced its withdrawal after a request to take 92 fin and 158 minke whales was turned down. It says that the IWC has changed from being an organization founded for the conservation and exploitation of whales to become purely a conservation organization. There has been an IWC ban on commercial whaling since 1986. Since the ban was upheld by the IWC at its meeting in July, Iceland formally withdrew from the Commission and, together with Norway, announced its intention to resume the commercial hunting of whales. Norway also declared its intention to begin a 3-year scientific research programme in July 1992 which will involve killing nearly 400 minke whales.

Before the meeting, the IWC's scientific committee had said that the population of minke whales had recovered sufficiently to allow the reintroduction of controlled commercial hunting of the species.

The European Community aims to join the IWC, to ensure that IWC rules are enshrined in EC law. If Norway continues whaling, it could be ineligible for EC membership.

RIVER DOLPHIN NUMBERS CONTINUE TO DECLINE

The baiji or Yangtze River dolphin in China continues to decline, chiefly as a result of entanglement with fishing gear and the destructive results of human disturbance. Its total population has now been estimated at fewer than 300. The Whale and Dolphin Conservation Society (WDCS) is funding research and conservation work to attempt to halt the decline of this endangered mammal, as well as introducing educational programmes for local people to inform them of the importance of the dolphins. The WDCS is also funding research into the equally threatened river dolphins in the Amazon.

DOLPHIN-DEADLY OR DOLPHIN-FRIENDLY TUNA

Following the outcry in the USA and UK at the revelation that millions of dolphins had been killed in the process of fishing for yellow-fin tuna, the tuna industry announced various agreements to move towards using 'dolphin-friendly' tuna. In autumn 1991 over three-quarters of the UK tuna industry signed an agreement after nearly a year of negotiations with the Whale and Dolphin Conservation Society.

The monitoring and implementation of the agreement has been patchy, however. Some companies have installed cannery inspectors while others are simply taking their suppliers on trust that the tuna are caught using 'dolphin-friendly' methods such as long-lining or pole and line fishing. Conservation organizations feel that in order for the agreement to be effective, observers must be placed at those locations where it is possible that drift-net-caught 'dolphin-deadly' tuna could be disguised as 'dolphin-friendly'. Until then, claims made by the various companies cannot be absolutely validated.

ILLEGAL BIRD TRADE KILLS UNKNOWN SPECIES

The Environmental Investigation Agency brought to light the case of four birds of a hitherto unknown species which were found dead in a bird trader's cage in Tanzania. The captives were to be sold as pets in the European Community. Although it is illegal for wild birds to be sold in the EC as well as Japan and the USA, no action has been taken in any of these countries to stop the trade, which results in the death of three out of four birds during their transit in what are often cramped and cruel conditions.

TRAFFIC CONDEMNS GREEK WILDLIFE TRADE

TRAFFIC, the wildlife monitoring agency, found hundreds of tourist shops on Greek islands selling wildlife products from endangered species. As a result of their report, the WWF condemned the Greek government for allowing trade in endangered species to flourish. Greece is not a signatory to CITES, which has banned the trade in objects made of jaguar and cheetah skin, sea turtle shells, ivory trinkets and stuffed rare birds, all of which TRAFFIC found in the tourist shops. As a member of the EC, however, Greece is obliged to implement any decisions made by CITES and should not allow trade to continue.

THE COMMUNICATORS AND EDUCATORS

ATTENBOROUGH LAUNCHES WATER GROUP

Sir David Attenborough is the head of a new organization, Water for Wildlife, launched early this year. The group is dedicated to campaigning for increased powers for the National Rivers Authority (NRA) and for awareness of the need for water conservation and recycling, especially important as drought conditions hit Britain once again. Through raising public awareness and bringing about changes to the NRA, Water for Wildlife hopes to benefit the many species which have declined as a result of drought, overextraction and pollution in Britain's rivers. These include swans, kingfishers, mayflies and dragonflies.

BELLAMY SIGNS MAGNA CARTA

To commemorate the 777th anniversary in June of the signing of the Magna Carta, the Conservation Foundation, led by David Bellamy, produced a New Magna Carta. This was drawn up to declare a commitment to Britain's living heritage, and the celebrity signatories — Bellamy, Robert Hardy, Sir George Trevelyan and Allen Meredith — signed the document underneath an ancient yew tree close to the historic site at Runnymede, where the original Magna Carta was signed.

The Conservation Foundation encouraged people across the country to organize their own local ceremonies where they could read the New Magna Carta aloud and swear an oath to support the environmental pledges which it lists. These pledges include a promise to use 50 per cent less energy and never to disturb natural environments or their wildlife. The document, written by David Bellamy, also contains a pledge that Britain 'will lead, not trail our fellow members of the expanding Europe when it comes to woodlands, forests and forestry'.

Money raised from selling copies of the New Magna Carta — some of which are in Latin — will be channelled into the Yew Tree Campaign for preserving Britain's ancient yew trees. The Conservation Foundation also intends to produce a gazette chronicling the age and location of these ancient trees throughout the UK, using information gathered from volunteers.

CALENDAR OF EVENTS

JANUARY '92

Indigenous peoples from Alaska form a coalition with the aim of persuading the scientific establishment to use their traditional methods of observing and understanding the natural world. They are particularly concerned about the decline of species in the Bering Sea, including fur seals, Steller's sea lions, cod and many seabirds.

In Scotland, the reintroduction of red kites is enhanced by the release of 20 birds from southern Sweden. An Environmental Change Network is established in the UK to monitor climate changes and their effects on wildlife and the land.

9 Once again, the EC warns the UK government that it will take legal action to protect Britain's outstanding landscapes from damaging development.

18 The United Nations Inter-governmental Panel on Climate Change (IPCC) says that pollution seems to be slowing the manmade global warming effect. However this atmospheric cooling is slight compared to the build-up of heat caused by a rising concentration of carbon dioxide gas, which is also produced when fossil fuels are burned. It is only likely to delay the warming by a few years.

19 The New Forest in Hampshire is officially declared to be a National Park.

20 It is announced that the new Queen's Award for Environmental Achievement is to be introduced next year.

22 Countryside campaigners react with dismay to a statement by the government that they fear would unleash a tide of new development. The Department of Environment insists however, that the new guidance on rural planning for local authorities throughout England and Wales does not mark a radical change in direction. The key change concerns the status of low-grade land which makes up two-thirds of farmland in England and Wales. The new guidance says that 'little weight' should be given to the loss of such poor-quality land.

FEBRUARY '92

A survey for the Countryside Commission reports that conditions in National Parks in England and Wales have deteriorated in the last 20 years.

Representatives of over 50 indigenous peoples from rainforests across the world meet in Malaysia to form an alliance. Their aim is to unite in their struggle against threats to their homelands.

12 A report argues that protection of the planet must be compatible with free trade. 'We must guard against the risk of the issue of the environment being kidnapped by trade protectionist interests,' argues Arthur Dunkel, Director-General of the General Agreement on Tariffs and Trade (GATT). 'If that happens, the world will lose out twice: through lost growth resulting from reduced trade and through ineffective environmental policies.'

14 Environmental campaigners occupy two bridges due for demolition in order to make way for the M3 extension through Twyford Down, Hampshire.

15 The Global Biodiversity Strategy is launched by the World Conservation Union (IUCN), the UN Environment Programme (UNEP) and the World Resources Institute. It suggests that Third World countries should declare ownership of their resources as a way of protecting the earth's diversity of species while allowing those countries to profit from the growing demand for their plants and animals.

16 Several hundred protesters gather at Twyford Down to protest at the M3 extension; six of them are arrested.

20 The WWF publishes a report on the effects of global warming on national parks and protected areas around the world. The report states that half their plant and animal life is at risk.

MARCH '92

A report for the International Council for Bird Preservation details the damage to wildlife arising from the fighting in Croatia. Birds, fish and mammals including red deer and boar are threatened as a consequence of the conflict.

In the Mediterranean, an alien species of seaweed spreads through the waters of the French and Italian Rivieras. The weed threatens to overwhelm native seagrass which is an important breeding ground for fish.

3 Environment Secretary Michael Heseltine announces plans to create the UK's largest nature reserve near Teesmouth in Cleveland. The reserve will cost £11 million and cover 10sq km of varied habitat.

14 The Department of Energy and Environment fails to set out how Britain will hit its target of stabilizing rising emissions of global warming carbon dioxide gas. The 12 EC environment ministers had each agreed to submit their nation's plans to stabilize carbon dioxide before April 1992.

27 A White House spokesman announces that the United States President, George Bush, will attend the Earth Summit in Rio de Janiero only if it produces a treaty serving US interests.

29 The educational charity Environmental Awareness Trust announces a £10 million plan to convert the Roundhouse in north London into the world's first 'environmental maze'. 'Earth Focus' will be a 5000sq m permanent exhibition. It is estimated that 500,000 visitors a year will enter this 'mental maze exploring environmental questions'.

Botanist Dr Philip Gates warns that British plants and wildlife are likely to be transformed by global warming. He states that species including bluebells, mountain hares and the great raft spider may disappear completely.

Norway and Russia increase their seal hunt quota from 51,000 to 60,000. Greenpeace protests that there is no scientific justification for the increase.

The prolonged drought in southern Africa is starting to kill large numbers of animals in southeast Zimbabwe. The hippopotamuses of Gonarezhou National Park, on the Mozambique border, may become extinct as a result, and elephant, kudu and eland are also at risk.

14 The Royal Society for Nature Conservation gives the three main political parties marks out of a hundred, based on a checklist of 20 key environmental commitments, from the manifestos issued during their general election campaigns. The Liberal Democrats score 42, Labour 32 and the Conservatives 27. It is also announced that the EC is to start legal action against Britain over two fresh allegations of breaches of European Environmental law. One concerns the pollution of the Carnon Valley and Falmouth Bay in Cornwall and the other the planting of 8sq km of conifers on Scottish moorland.

17 Earth First! members gather in Brighton for their first conference. The newest and most radical environmental group in Britain, now with 1000 UK sympathizers, has already established a reputation for direct and confrontational action.

18 Maurice Strong, head of June's Earth Summit, hosts a meeting of 'eminent people' in Tokyo, Japan, to iron out the massive disagreements that still divide nations.

22 In a blunt speech, Prince Charles criticizes both the wealthy, developed countries and the Third World for failing to show the good faith, flexibility and sense of common purpose needed to cope with what he is certain is an onrushing global environmental crisis.

28 In a speech to the World Bank and International Monetary Fund, the UK Chancellor signals Britain's readiness to back increased funding for developing countries.

29 It is confirmed that Britain, America and other industrialized countries are to admit their responsibility for causing most of the world's pollution and for bearing the main burden of cleaning it up. Their pledge will be declared at the United Nations Earth Summit in June.

The world's space nations agree to a joint programme using new satellites and a dozen existing ones to measure global changes in the environment.

6 No 'green' legislation is announced in the Queen's speech at the opening of Parliament. Most noticeable by its absence is any commitment to set up an environmental protection agency — this was the centrepiece of the environmental section of the Conservative election manifesto.

7 Researchers at the Institute of Terrestrial Ecology reveal that 9.4 per cent of Britain's hedgerows were destroyed between 1984-1990. This loss of hedgerows has damaging implications for wildlife.

14 Britain faces the first heatwave of the summer with temperatures reaching 25°C.

18 A World Bank report states that educating girls is the biggest single solution to problems of poverty and environmental destruction as women control their fertility. A UK government spokesman claims that building roads often helps, not harms, the environment. Bypassing of towns and villages, environmental assessments prior to choosing routes and the planting of trees and shrubs were 'often good news for the environment... There are some that argue that expansion of the road network will be devastating for the environment. They are wrong.' These claims draw immediate criticism from environmental groups, including Friends of the Earth.

JUNE '92

Conservationists criticize changes to hunting laws by the Italian government. Under the new regulations, regional authorities have greater powers to alter both hunting season deadlines and the boundaries of protected areas. Migrant birds may be hunted five days a week.

Seals, dolphins and other marine mammals are washed up dead on the eastern coasts of the USA and in the Gulf of Mexico. Most have apparently died from the phocine distemper virus.

Local authorities in Hargeisa, Somalia's second city, appeal for international aid when dieldrin, malathion and other deadly pesticides leach into water supplies. These came from the operations base of East Africa's Desert Locust Control Organization, which was abandoned in 1988 as a result of the country's civil war.

The United Nations Earth Summit takes place in Rio de Janiero. See the feature on page 74 for details.

18 In the wake of protests from the IUCN and local people, the government of Botswana cancels an intended major dredging programme in the Okavango Delta, a site of unique importance to wildlife. Their plans to alter the River Boro and increase water supplies to the towns of Maun and Orapa were based upon flawed calculations.

20 Chemical giant ICI announces that it will cease production of halon, a fire-fighting chemical, at its plant in Runcorn, Merseyside. Halon is known to be a major cause of ozone depletion.

25 The UK government holds talks with leading conservation groups over the Darwin Initiative. This plan to strengthen international protection for species at risk was announced by the Prime Minister, John Major, at the Earth Summit. It aims to draw together the expertise of such institutions as The Royal Botanic Gardens at Kew, the World Conservation Monitoring Centre and the International Council for Bird Preservation (both based at Cambridge), and the Natural History Museum in London, to help Third World countries to set up conservation programmes.

29 Start of the 44th annual meeting of the International Whaling Commission (IWC) in Glasgow.

JULY '92

The red squirrel faces extinction in southern Britain, according to the Forestry Commission. It will also continue to decline in the north unless large areas of conifer forest are maintained. The Commission suggests setting up protection areas consisting of large expanses of mixed-species coniferous forest.

Hundreds of dolphins are reportedly drowning in the Mediterranean through being trapped in drift-nets used by South Korean fishing vessels to catch tuna and swordfish.

It is announced that a total of 84 airlines, including many of the major carriers, have agreed to ban wild-caught birds from their flights.

Former Soviet President Mikhail Gorbachev is to head 'Green Cross' — a new organization which aims to be the environmental equivalent of the Red Cross.

3 The IWC conference concludes with a decision to maintain the ban on commercial whaling for another year.

6 Scientists state that Lake Victoria in Africa is dying. Only three types of fish exist in the lake, compared with 38 in the 1970s. Researchers blame the introduction in 1960 of the Nile perch, which preys voraciously on other fish.

11 The Canadian government bans cod fishing on the Grand Banks off Newfoundland and Labrador. The numbers of spawning cod are some of the lowest ever recorded.

16 English Nature launches a recovery programme to reintroduce the dormouse, which is currently restricted to a few sites in the south and west. It plans to study the dormouse's habits through the use of radio-tracking equipment.

26 A Greenpeace study announces that a third of the population of England suffer health risks as a result of air pollution.

AUGUST '92

A combination of ideal weather conditions and the careful management of protected sites has resulted in a record breeding season for several of Britain's rarest birds, according to the RSPB. Among those which have reproduced successfully are birds of prey, including ospreys, marsh harriers and red kites — the latter having their most successful year for a century, with 79 breeding pairs in Wales raising 93 chicks.

A major logging, pulp and paper project planned for the Merauké area of Irian Jaya, Indonesia, may be abandoned following the withdrawal of one of the two companies supporting it. The project would have involved the clear-felling of 800,000 hectares of tropical forest and its replacement by eucalyptus plantations. It had been widely denounced as disastrous both for the environment and for the local Auyu forest people. After a Survival International campaign, PT Astra, Indonesia's second largest company, pulled out.

New evidence suggests that the destruction of peat bogs is adding to the greenhouse effect. A report commissioned by Friends of the Earth suggests that peat bogs act as vast carbon stores. Cutting them for fuel or compost, or draining and ploughing them for farming and forestry, triggers large emissions of carbon dioxide, equivalent to 40 per cent of the total produced by cars.

Some of California's most renowned bathing beaches have been closed due to pollution from coliform bacteria — a result of untreated sewage leaking into offshore waters.

SEPTEMBER '92

First meeting of pro-whaling body, North Atlantic Marine Mammal Commission, formed by Norway, Iceland, Greenland and the Faroes.

4 National Bat Conference. Experts and amateurs come together to discuss the habits and future of bats in Britain.

9 The RSPB launches its 'Campaign for the Countryside' aimed at reforming agricultural policies to recreate habitats and save areas under threat.

10 Start of the Green Party's Annual General Meeting and Conference in Wolverhampton.

18 The Marine Conservation Society Conference takes place at the University of Nottingham. Topics covered include the effects of the Gulf War.

21 The European Environment Conference seeks to tackle the developments in environmental policy and practice throughout Europe.

27 'Forbidden Britain Day', when ramblers stage protest walks on areas of countryside where public access is normally restricted.

OCTOBER '92

4 WWF's 'Walk for Forests of the World' takes place nationwide, to raise funds for the world's forests.

5 Start of International Elephant Week, which celebrates the 1989 ban on trade in elephant ivory.

NOVEMBER '92

Montreal Protocol meeting on protecting the ozone layer, attended by the world's industrialized and developing nations. Major topics of debate include CFCs, halons and other ozone-depleters.

26 National Tree Week. To celebrate the 40th anniversary of the Queen's accession to the throne, thousands of groups of 40 trees are planted by voluntary organizations, schools, local authorities, companies and individuals across the country.

30 Basel Convention meeting. Signatory states of this ambitious, but so far ineffective, convention on the transportation of toxic waste meet in an effort to tighten up its provisions.

DECEMBER '92

11 EC heads of government meet in Edinburgh for second of this year's EC summits. Reform of the Common Agricultural Policy is one of the topics under discussion.

EVENTS IN '93

Three UN resolutions come into effect that ban the use of drift nets, which are blamed for large-scale deaths of dolphins and other small cetaceans.

JANUARY
Catalytic converters become compulsory on all new petrol vehicles in the UK.

JUNE
Deadline for the UK government to submit its plans to the EC concerning the conservation and reconstruction of the countryside.

AUGUST
The Environment Northern Seas Conference to be held in Norway. The conference will attempt to find practical solutions to the various environmental problems that cross national boundaries.

A GUIDE TO PROTECTED SPECIES

Protection is given to animal species nationally and internationally through laws and treaties. Important in any attempt to protect animals is their classification: as rare, or endangered, for example.

IUCN CATEGORIZATION

The World Conservation Union (IUCN) categorizes animals according to the degree to which they are threatened. The IUCN categories are reproduced below.

EXTINCT

Taxa (groups of animals) not definitely located in the wild during the past 50 years (criterion as used by CITES).

ENDANGERED

Taxa in danger of extinction and whose survival is unlikely if the causal factors continue operating.

Included are taxa whose numbers have been so drastically reduced that they are deemed to be in immediate danger of extinction. Also included are taxa that may be extinct but have definitely been seen in the wild in the past 50 years.

VULNERABLE

Taxa believed likely to move into the 'Endangered' category if the causal factors continue operating.

Included are taxa of which most or all the populations are decreasing because of over-exploitation, extensive destruction of habitat or other environmental disturbance; taxa with populations that have been seriously depleted and whose ultimate security has not yet been assured; and taxa with populations that are still abundant but are under threat from severe adverse factors throughout their range.

NB In practice, 'Endangered' and 'Vulnerable' categories may include, temporarily, taxa whose populations are beginning to recover as a result of remedial action, but whose recovery is insufficient to justify their transfer to another category.

RARE

Taxa with small world populations that are not at present 'Endangered' or 'Vulnerable', but which are at risk.

These taxa are usually localized within restricted geographical areas or habitats or are thinly scattered over a more extensive range.

INDETERMINATE

Taxa *known* to be 'Endangered', 'Vulnerable' or 'Rare' but where there is not enough information to say which of the three categories is appropriate.

INSUFFICIENTLY KNOWN

Taxa that are *suspected* but not definitely known to belong to any of the above categories, because of lack of information.

COMMERCIALLY THREATENED

Taxa not currently threatened with extinction, but most or all of whose populations are threatened as a sustainable commercial resource, or will become so, unless their exploitation is regulated. This category applies only to taxa whose populations are assumed to be relatively large.

THE WILDLIFE AND COUNTRYSIDE ACT

The Wildlife and Countryside Act of 1981 covers the protection of rare and endangered plant and animal species in the UK. The animals (listed on the opposite page) are protected under Schedule 5 of the Act under which it is illegal to kill, injure, take or sell any of those listed without a special licence. 14 species were added to Schedule 5 in July 1992, and all the schedules are regularly revised.

Mammals listed under Schedule 6 of the Act receive additional protection. It is illegal to kill or take by certain methods the species listed under this schedule.

CITES

Species listed under CITES Appendix 1 are threatened with extinction, and trade in them is permitted only in exceptional circumstances. Mammals with Appendix 1 status are listed on the right.

WILDLIFE AND COUNTRYSIDE ACT: SCHEDULE 5

European adder
Bats, horseshoe (all species)
Bats, typical (all species)
Beetle, *Graphoderus zonatus*
Beetle, *Hyperbaeus flavipes*
Beetle, *Paracymus aeneus*
Beetle, rainbow leaf
Beetle, lesser silver water
Beetle, mire pill
Burbot
Butterfly, chequered skipper
Butterfly, heath fritillary
Butterfly, high brown fritillary
Butterfly, large blue
Butterfly, swallowtail
Cricket, field
Cricket, mole
Dolphin, bottle-nose

Dolphin, common
Dragonfly, Norfolk aeshna
Frog, common (limited protection)
Grasshopper, wart-biter
Lizard, sand
Lizard, viviparous (limited protection)
Moth, barberry carpet
Moth, black-veined
Moth, Essex emerald
Moth, New Forest burnet
Moth, reddish bluff
Moth, Sussex emerald
Newt, great crested (warty newt)
Newt, palmate (limited protection)
Newt, smooth (limited protection)
Northern hatchet shell
Otter
Pink sea fan

Porpoise, harbour (common porpoise)
Sea-slug, lagoon
Slow-worm (limited protection)
Snail, Carthusian
Snail, De Folin's
Snail, glutinous
Snail, lagoon
Snail, sandbowl
Snake, grass (limited protection)
Snake, smooth
Spider, fen raft
Spider, ladybird
Squirrel, red
Sturgeon
Toad, common (limited protection)
Toad, natterjack
Worm, tentacled lagoon

WILDLIFE AND COUNTRYSIDE ACT: SCHEDULE 6

Badger
Bats, horseshoe (all species)
Bats, typical (all species)
Cat, wild
Dolphin, bottle-nose

Dolphin, common
Dormice (all species)
Hedgehog
Marten, pine
Otter

Polecat
Porpoise, harbour (common porpoise)
Shrews (all species)
Squirrel, red

CITES APPENDIX 1

Addax
African wild ass
Anteater, banded (numbat)
Armadillo, giant
Babirusa
Bear, Asiatic black
Bear, Malayan sun
Bear, spectacled
Bettong (bush-tailed kangaroo)
Black-footed ferret
Buffalo, wood
Bush dog
Cat, flat-headed
Cat, mountain
Cheetah
Chinchilla (wild)
Chimpanzee
Chimpanzee, pygmy
Deer, swamp
Deer, pampas
Dolphin, Yangtze river
Elephant, African
Elephant, Asiatic
Gibbon (all species)
Goral, common

Gorilla
Hispid hare (bristly rabbit)
Hog, pygmy
Huemel, Chilean
Huemel, Peruvian
Jaguar
Lemur (all species)
Leopard, clouded
Leopard, snow
Macaque, lion-tailed
Mainland serow
Manatee, Amazon
Manatee, American
Monkey, brown howler
Monkey, proboscis
Monkey, uakari (3 species)
Monkey, woolly spider
Orang-utan
Oryx, Arabian (white oryx)
Oryx, scimitar
Otter
Otter, giant
Otter, marine
Otter, South American river
Otter, southern river

Panda, giant
Pangolin, Cape
Prairie dog, Mexican
Pronghorn (US races)
Pudu, southern
Rhinoceros, black
Rhinoceros, Sumatran
Rhinoceros, great Indian
Rhinoceros, Javan (lesser one-horned rhinoceros)
Susu (Ganges river dolphin)
Tapir, Asian
Tapir, Baird's
Tapir, mountain
Tiger
Urial
Vicuña
Whale, bowhead
Whale, right
Whale, sperm
Zebra, Cape mountain
Zebra, Grevy's

FURTHER READING

Alexander, R McNeill,
Locomotion of Animals,
Blackwell 1982

Apa Insight Guides,
Southeast Asian Wildlife,
Apa Publications 1991

Beebee, Trevor, *Pond Life,*
Whittet Books 1992

Blackburn, J,
Charles Waterton: Traveller &
Conservationist,
Random House 1991

Brown, Michael & May, John,
The Greenpeace Story,
Dorling Kindersley, 2nd edn. 1991

Burton, Robert, *Bird Flight,*
Facts on File 1990

Burton, Robert, *Bird Migration,*
Facts on File, 1992

Burton, Robert,
RSPB Birdfeeder Handbook,
RSPB 1990

Chanin, Paul,
The Natural History of Otters,
Academic Press 1988

Collins, Mark, ed.,
The Last Rain Forests,
Mitchell Beazley, in association
with IUCN 1990

Cox, Daniel J, *Black Bear,*
Hale, 1990

Crawford, A K,
Otter Survey of Wales,
Vincent Wildlife Trust, Chronicle
Books 1991

Darwin, Charles,
The Voyage of the Beagle,
Penguin 1989

Dewey, Donald,
Bears: A Photographic Survey,
Headline 1991

Doak, Wade, *Encounters with*
Whales & Dolphins, Hodder 1991

Domico, Terry & Newman,
Mark, *Bears of the World,*
Facts on File 1988

Downer, John, *Supersense,*
BBC Books 1988

Evans, David, *History of Natural*
Conservation in Britain,
Routledge 1992

Evans, Peter, *The Natural History*
of Whales & Dolphins,
Christopher Helm 1987

Evans, Peter, *Whales,* Whittet 1990

Fenech, Natalino, *Fatal Flight,*
Quiller Press 1992 (documents the
annual slaughter of migratory
birds on Malta)

Ford, A., *John James Audubon:*
A Biography, Abbeville 1988

Ford, Emma, *Falconry,*
Shire Publications, 1984

Ford, Emma, *Falconry: Art &*
Practice, Blandford Press 1992

Forsyth, Adrian, Fogden,
Michael & Fogden, Patricia,
Portraits of the Rainforest,
Hale 1991

Foster-Thurley, P, MacDonald, S
& Mason, C, *Otters: An Action*
Plan for their Conservation,
Vincent Wildlife Trust, 1990
IUCN, 1991

Garner, J F & Jones, B L,
Countryside Law,
Shaw & Sons, 1987 (UK, covering
planning, access, protection of
wildlife and pollution)

Gray, J, *Animal Locomotion,*
Blackwell 1982

Green, T & R, *Otter Survey of*
Scotland, Harrison, Sir Richard,
Merehurst 1988

Gubbay, Dr S, *Future of the Coast,*
MCS 1990

Jackson, Michael H, *Galapagos: A*
Natural History Guide, Bradt 1985

Lea, John, *Tourism & Development*
in the Third World, Routledge
1988, Dorling Kindersley 1990

Leatherwood, Stephen &
Reeves, Randall R.,
The Sierra Club Handbook of
Whales & Dolphins of the World,
Sierra Club 1983

Lovelock, J E, *Gaia,* Oxford, 1987

Lyster, Simon, *International*
Wildlife Law, Grotius 1985

Martin, Tony, *Whales & Dolphins,*
Salamander 1990

Mason, C F & MacDonald, S M,
Otters: Ecology & Conservation,
Cambridge University Press 1986

McGoodwin, James R,
Crisis in the World's Fisheries,
Stanford University Press 1990

Meadows, D H & D, Randers,
Jorgen, *Beyond the Limits,*
Earthscan Publications 1992

Mech, David, *The Way of the Wolf,*
Swan Hill Press 1992

Merrill, L, *The Romance of*
Victorian Natural History,
Oxford University Press 1989

Mitchell, Andrew,
The Enchanted Canopy: Secrets
from the Rainforest Roof,
Collins 1986

Monbiot, George,
Poisoned Arrows: An Investigative
Journey through Indonesia,
Michael Joseph 1989

Newman, Arnold, *Tropical*
Rainforest, Facts on File 1990

Nightingale, Neil, *New Guinea,*
an Island Apart, BBC Books 1992

Parry-Jones, Jemima, *Falconry,*
David & Charles 1988

Pearce, Fred, *Green Warriors,* Bodley Head 1991

Rose, Chris *Dirty Man of Europe,* Simon & Schuster 1990

Ross, Karen, *Okavango, Jewel of the Kalahari,* BBC Books 1987

Salathé, Tobias, ed., *Conserving Migratory Birds,* International Council for Bird Preservation, Cambridge 1991

Samstag, Tony, *For Love of Birds: The Story of the Royal Society for the Protection of Birds 1889-1988,* RSPB books 1988

Sandys-Winsch, G *Animal Law,* Shaw & Sons 1984

Scarce, Rik, *Eco-Warriors,* Noble Press 1990

Smith, Geoffrey, *The Joy of Wildlife Gardening,* RSPB 1989

Steadman, D W & Zousmer, S, *Galapagos: Discovery on Darwin's Islands,* Airlife 1988

Sterry, Paul, *Wildlife Travelling Companion: East Africa,* Crowood Press 1992

Strachan, R, Birks, J D S, Chanin, P R F & Jefferies, D J, *Otter Survey of England 1984-86,* English Nature 1990

Swanson, Timothy & Barbier, Edward B, *Economics for the Wilds: Wildlife, Wildlands, Diversity & Development,* Earthscan 1992

Terborgh, John, *Where Have All the Birds Gone?* Princeton University Press 1989

Village, Andrew, *Falcons,* Whittet 1992

Wayre, P, *The Private Life of the Otter,* Batsford 1979

Wellnhofer, Peter, *The Illustrated Encyclopedia of Pterosaurs,* Salamander 1991

Whitley, Edward, *Gerald Durrell's Army,* John Murray 1992

COMPETITIONS

The Ansorge Award
Organized by the Amateur Entomologists Society for the Best Junior Exhibit at the Society's Annual Exhibition.
Entries in October.

Bird Yearlist
Sponsoring competition run by the British Trust for Ornithology, which provides a booklet for competitors' bird count over a year.
Entries in January, results February.
First prize: Pair of Leica binoculars worth £650.

The Blake Shield
Run by the British Naturalists Association for groups of people 8–16 years with adult leaders in natural history projects.
Entries in June.
First prize: Residential visit to a Field Centre.

BP Conservation Expedition Award
The International Council for Bird Preservation, the Fauna and Flora Preservation Society and the Conservation Expedition Competition offer a total of £20,000 in grant funding for expeditions involving people in the following categories: Tropical Forests, Wetland, Oceanic Islands and Marine and Globally Threatened Species.
First prize: £3000 (half of which should be intended for local people in the relevant countries who helped or supported the expedition).

The Hammond Award
Organized by the Amateur Entomologists Society for the most useful article published during the year in the Society's bulletin.

Nature Writing
Essay competition run by BBC Wildlife Magazine in association with BBC Radio 4's Natural History Programme.
Entries by May, results July.
First Prize: £1000 for the best essay by a professional, a semi-professional or an amateur writer.
£400 for the best essay by an amateur writer, presented only if the top award is won by a professional writer.
£200 for the best essay by a young writer aged between 13 and 17.
£100 for the best essay by a writer aged 12 or younger.

Wildlife Photographer of the Year
Organized by *BBC Wildlife* magazine, the Natural History Museum and the Fauna and Flora Preservation Society.
Entries by June, results publicized in August.
First prize: Wildlife Photograph of the Year, £1500.
Wildlife Photographer of the Year, £2500.

Young Wildlife Photographer of the Year
Organized as above. Open to photographers 17 years and under.
Entry dates as above.
First prize: £300.

DIRECTORY OF ORGANIZATIONS

Ark Environmental Foundation
PO Box 18
Melbourne
Royston
Hertfordshire SG8 6JQ
✆ 081 968 6780
Provides information and a framework for community action to benefit the natural environment.

Council of Europe
Centre Naturopa
Conseil de l'Europe
BP 431 R 6
F 67006 Strasbourg
France
✆ 010 33 88 61 49 61
Steering committee for Conservation and Management of the Environment and Natural Resources throughout Europe.

Environmental Investigation Agency
2nd Floor
2 Peartree Court
London EC1R 0DS
✆ 071 490 7040
A non-profitmaking investigative organization working to protect wildlife and the environment throughout the world.

European Commission DG X1 (Environment)
Division B3 EC
Rue de la Loi 200
1049 Brussels
Belgium
Responsible for European Community environmental policy.

European Institute of Ecology
1 Rue des Recollets
BP 4005 – 57040
Metz
Cedex
France
Tackles ecological issues throughout Europe.

Fauna and Flora Preservation Society
1 Kensington Gore
London SW7 2AR
✆ 071 823 8899
Promotes the conservation of wild animals and plants throughout the world.

Friends of the Earth International
Veriniging Milieudefensie
Tacovanden Heiligenberg
Damrak 26
1012 LJ
Amsterdam
The Netherlands
✆ 010 31 20 622 1386
International pressure group which campaigns vigorously for the protection of the environment and the for the promotion of sustainable alternative sources of fuel and economic practices.

Gaia Foundation
18 Well Walk
London NW3 1LD
✆ 071 435 5000
Provides funding to support indigenous populations, mainly those inhabiting the South American rainforests.

Greenpeace International
Keizersgracht 176
1016 DW Amsterdam
The Netherlands
✆ 010 31 205 236555
Campaigns against abuse of the environment through lobbying and non-violent direct action protests.

Groundwork Foundation
85–87 Cornwall Street
Birmingham B3 3BY
✆ 021 236 8565
Restores local landscapes and habitats, especially urban wastelands, working with communities, businesses and local authorities.

Institute for European Environmental Policy (IEEP)
158 Buckingham Palace Road
London SW1W 9TR
✆ 071 824 8787
Analyzes and reports on environmental policy throughout Europe and promotes awareness of environment protection.

Institute of Terrestrial Ecology
Monks Wood
Abbots Ripton
Huntingdon
Cambridgeshire PE17 2LS
✆ 04873 381
Researches into ecosystems, surveys land use and vegetation and investigates environmental problem areas.

International Council for Bird Preservation (ICBP)
32 Cambridge Road
Girton
Cambridge CB3 0PJ
✆ 0223 277318
Campaigns to protect the world's birds and their habitats.

International Foundation for the Conservation of Birds
11300 Weddington Street
North Hollywood
California 91601
USA
Campaigns to conserve birds in the USA and the rest of the world.

International Primate Protection League (IPPL)
116 Judd Street
London WC1H 9NS
✆ 071 837 7227
Works exclusively to protect primates throughout the world.

International Waterfowl and Wetlands Research Bureau (IWRB)
Slimbridge
Gloucestershire GL2 7BT
✆ 0453 890634
Promotes research into, and the conservation of wetlands.

International Whaling Commission (IWC)
135 Station Road
Histon
Cambridge CB4 4NP
✆ 0223 233971
An intergovernmental organization which reviews measures to protect whales. Collects and disseminates data on whales.

International Wildlife Coalition (UK)
PO Box 73
Hartfield
Sussex TN7 4EY
✆ 0342 825482
Promotes research into wildlife and natural habitat destruction.

People's Trust for Endangered Species
Suite 9
Hamble House
Mead Row
Godalming
Surrey GU7 3JX
✆ 0483 424848
Aims to conserve the environment through the protection of animals, plants and wild places.

Population Concern
231 Tottenham Court Road
London W1P 9AE
✆ 071 631 1546
Campaigns to raise awareness of the dangers of population growth, and promotes planned parenthood.

Rainforest Foundation
2 Ingate Place
Battersea
London SW8 3NS
✆ 071 498 7603
Works to protect large areas of Amazonia and its natural inhabitants.

Society for Wildlife Art of the Nations
Wallsworth Hall
Twigworth
Gloucestershire GL2 9PA
✆ 0452 731422
Aims to link artists with conservation.

Survival International
310 Edgware Road
London W2 1DY
✆ 071 723 5535
Works for the rights of threatened tribal peoples worldwide.

United Nations Ecology Programme (UNEP) UK
3 Endsleigh Street
London WC1H 0DD
✆ 071 388 2117
Monitors and assesses changes in the world's physical (human and natural) state. Coordinates international action.

World Conservation Monitoring Centre
219c Huntingdon Road
Cambridge CB3 0DL
✆ 0223 277314
Collects and disseminates information on animals and plants, especially endangered species.

World Conservation Union (IUCN — International Union for the Conservation of Nature and Natural Resources)
Rue Mauverney 28
1196 Gland
Geneva
Switzerland
✆ 010 41 223 9114
An independent alliance of over 120 countries uniting on equal terms to tackle conservation and the use of natural resources, according to the World Conservation Strategy (1980) as a basis for priorities for action.

World Wide Fund for Nature International (WWF)
1196 Gland
Geneva
Switzerland
℅ 010 41 223 7181
Campaigns and raises money for conservation of wildlife and wild places and promotes the wise use of the earth's resources.

Worldwatch Institute
1776 Massachusetts Avenue NW
Washington DC20036
USA
℅ 010 1 202 452 1999
Informs governments and the public of environmental issues, seen from a global perspective.

UK ORGANIZATIONS
General

Alternative Technology Association
Centre for Alternative Technology
Machynlleth
Powys SY20 9AZ
℅ 0654 702400
Promotes and encourages the development and use of alternative technology in the UK.

Amateur Entomologists Society
22 Salisbury Road
Feltham
Middlesex TW13 5DP
℅ 081 890 3584
Promotes the study of all species of insect, particularly for young amateurs.

Army Ornithological Society
Rose Cottage
Bottlesford
Pewsey
Wiltshire SN9 6LU
℅ 0672 851403
Aims to encourage birdwatching and the science of ornithology in the British Army.

Association for the Protection of Rural Scotland
Gladstone's Land
483 Lawnmarket
Edinburgh EH1 2NT
℅ 031 225 7013
Informs and influences public opinion on issues which relate to the protection of Scotland's countryside.

Association of British Wild Animal Keepers
12 Tackley Road
Eastville
Bristol BS5 6UQ
Provides help and advice to the keepers of wild animals in Britain and provides a forum for discussion.

Association of National Parks and Countryside Voluntary Wardens
25 The High Gate
Newcastle upon Tyne NE3 4LS
℅ 091 285 8570
Provides a forum for wardens, to provide information and to improve the management of Britain's national parks.

Barn Owl Trust
Waterleat
Ashburton
Devon TQ13 7HU
℅ 0364 53026
Works to conserve the barn owl and its natural environment throughout the UK.

Bat Conservation Trust
London Ecology Centre
45 Shelton Street
London WC2H 9HJ
℅ 071 240 0933
Conducts research and conservation projects, and aims to increase public awareness and appreciation of bats and their needs.

Bird Line (Bird Information Service)
Stonerunner
Coast Road
Cley-next-the-Sea
Holt,
Norfolk NR25 7RZ
℅ 0263 741139
Telephone service giving information on the status of all rare birds in Britain.

Black Environment Network
National Council for Voluntary Organizations
Regents Wharf
8 All Saints Street
London N1 9RL
℅ 071 713 6161
Aims to promote environmental awareness in the black community and supports active conservation projects.

Botanical Society of the British Isles (BSBI)
℅ Department of Botany
Natural History Museum
Cromwell Road
London SW7 5BD
℅ 071 589 6323 Extn 8701
Encourages amateurs and professionals to study and conserve British and Irish flowering plants.

British Antarctic Survey
High Cross
Madingley Road
Cambridge CB3 0ET
℅ 0223 61188
Carries out scientific research into Antarctica and the Southern Ocean and studies of the upper atmosphere and ozone layer.

British Association for Shooting and Conservation
Marford Mill
Rossett
Clwyd LL12 0HL
℅ 0244 570881
Promotes safety in game shooting and encourages the management of habitats for the benefit of all wildlife.

British Association of Nature Conservationists
PO Box 14
Neston
S Wirral L64 7UP
A forum for discussion for all groups and individuals concerned with conservation.

British Butterfly Conservation Society
P O Box 222
Dedham
Colchester
Essex CO7 6EY
℅ 0509 412870
Sponsors study and research, and encourages the protection of British butterflies.

British Ecological Society
26 Blades Court
Deodar Road
London SW15 2NU
℅ 081 871 9797
Promotes research in ecology and disseminates results.

British Herpetological Society
C/o London Zoo
Regents Park
London NW1 4RY
℅ 071 722 3333
Promotes the scientific study of reptiles and amphibians.

British Naturalists Association
48 Russell Way
Higham Ferrers
Northamptonshire NN9 8EJ
℅ 0933 314672
Educates the public in the protection of wildlife and landscapes and encourages the study of natural history.

British Ornithologists Union
C/o Natural History Museum
Sub-department of Ornithology
Tring
Hertfordshire HP23 6AP
℅ 0442 890080
Promotes the study of birds worldwide.

British Trust for Conservation Volunteers (BTCV)
36 St Mary's Street
Wallingford
Oxfordshire OX10 0EU
℅ 0491 39766
Organizes practical conservation work for volunteers of all ages, on a local and national level.

British Trust for Ornithology (BTO)
The Nunnery
Nunnery Place
Thetford
Norfolk IP24 2PU
℅ 0842 750050
Encourages the serious study of British wild birds and advises on their conservation.

British Waterfowl Association
Gill Cottage
New Gill
Bishopdale
Leyburn
North Yorkshire DL8 3TQ
℅ 0969 663693
Provides advice on keeping, breeding and conserving all types of waterfowl.

Care for the Wild
1 Ashfolds
Horsham Road
Rusper
West Sussex RH12 4QX
℅ 0293 871596
Works to alleviate cruelty to, and suffering of, wildlife.

Common Ground
45 Shelton Street
London WC2H 9HJ
℅ 071 379 3109
Champions the cause of common animals, plants and local landscapes.

Conchological Society of Great Britain and Ireland
C/o Hon. Secretary
51 Wynchwood Avenue
Luton
Bedfordshire LU2 7HT
Devoted to the serious study of molluscs, from slugs to mussels.

Conservation Foundation
1 Kensington Gore
London SW7 2AR
℅ 071 823 8842
Encourages industry and businesses to support and sponsor the conservation projects that it conducts.

The Conservation Trust
George Palmer Site
Northumberland Avenue
Reading RG2 7PW
℅ 0734 868442
A public information and education service. Collects and disseminates data on the global environment.

Council for Environmental Education (CEE)
University of Reading
London Road
Reading
Berkshire RG1 5AQ
℅ 0734 756061
Promotes environmental education, especially in the youth and school sectors.

Council for National Parks
246 Lavender Hill
London SW11 1LJ
℃ 071 924 4077
Undertakes research and publishes results, lobbies government and appears at public inquiries. Offers information and answers general enquiries about National Parks in Britain.

Council for the Protection of Rural England (CPRE)
Warwick House
25 Buckingham Palace Road
London SW1W 0PP
℃ 071 976 6433
Promotes the improvement and protection of the English countryside.

Campaign for the Protection of Rural Wales
Ty Gwyn
31 High Street
Welshpool
Powys SY21 7JP
℃ 0938 552525
Promotes the improvement and protection of the Welsh countryside.

The Country Trust
Denham Hill Farmhouse
Quainton
Aylesbury
Buckinghamshire HP22 4AN
℃ 0296 641708
Organizes and conducts visits to the British countryside for deprived inner city children.

Countryside Commission
John Dower House
Crescent Place
Cheltenham
Gloucestershire GL50 3RA
℃ 0242 521381
Advises both central and local government on all major issues dealing with rural conservation and recreation.

Countryside Council for Wales
Plas Penrhos
Penrhos Road
Bangor
Gwynedd LL57 2LQ
℃ 0248 370444
The new government conservation organization which replaced the Countryside Commission and Nature Conservancy Council in Wales from April 1992.

Countryside Education Trust
John Montagu Building
Beaulieu
Hampshire SO42 7ZN
℃ 0590 612340
Works to make the countryside accessible to all and promotes a more caring and informed attitude to the British countryside.

Countryside Venture
Lime Tree
Asherington
Totnes
Devon TQ9 7UL
℃ 0803 732562
Country training centres which advise and train people in practical management and rural skills, and provide a focus for development and alternative land use possibilities.

Department of the Environment (Wildlife Division)
Tollgate House
Houlton Street
Bristol BS2 9DJ
℃ 0272 218233
Government body responsible for the administration of zoos, environmental education, conservation of species and their habitat, and trade in endangered species.

Department of the Environment for Northern Ireland
Calvert House
23 Castle Place
Belfast BT1 1FY
℃ 0232 230560
The Countryside and Wildlife Branch is responsible for the conservation of wildlife and the environment and for the designation of important areas.

Durrell Institute of Conservation and Ecology
University of Kent
Canterbury CT2 7NX
℃ 0227 475480
An academic institution associated with the University of Kent, undertaking research and post graduate teaching in conservation biology.

Earthwatch Europe
Belsyre Court
57 Woodstock Road
Oxford OX2 6HU
℃ 0865 311600
Organizes 'green' holidays which allow members of the public to participate in research and scientific field studies.

Edward Grey Institute of Field Ornithology
Department of Zoology
South Parks Road
Oxford OX1 3PS
℃ 0865 271275
An academic institution associated with the University of Oxford Department of Zoology.

Elefriends
Coldharbour
Dorking
Surrey RH5 6HA
℃ 0306 713320
Works for the conservation and protection of elephants.

English Nature
Northminster House
Peterborough PE1 1UA
℃ 0733 340345
Government conservation organization which replaced the former NCC for England in April 1992.

Environment Council (formerly CoEnCo)
80 York Way
London N1 9AG
℃ 071 278 4736
Coordinates the national activities of the voluntary conservation movement and provides a forum for discussion on environmental issues.

Environmental Data Services
Finsbury Business Centre
40 Bowling Green Lane
London EC1R 0NE
℃ 071 278 7624
Information service for businesses. Publishes the monthly ENDS Report.

Farming and Wildlife Advisory Group
Stoneleigh
Kenilworth
Warwickshire CV8 2RX
℃ 0203 696699
Promotes the conservation of wildlife within the farmed countryside and advises farmers on how to incorporate conservation into modern agricultural techniques.

Field Studies Council
Preston Montford
Montford Bridge
Shrewsbury
Shropshire SY4 1HW
℃ 0743 850674
Aims to promote understanding and appreciation of the natural environment and its wildlife through education, often in residential field courses.

Fish Conservation Centre
Easter Cringate
Stirling FK7 9QX
℃ 0786 51312
Promotes research and practical management projects for the conservation of fish.

Foreign Birdwatching Reports and Information Service
C/o Steve Whitehouse
5 Stanway Close
Blackpole
Worcester WR4 9XL
℃ 0905 54541
A birdwatcher's reports and information service.

Forestry Commission
231 Corstorphine Road
Edinburgh EH12 7AT
℃ 031 334 0303
The national forestry authority in the UK, the Commission administers legislation concerning forestry. It also offers advice to private foresters.

Friends of the Earth (England, Wales and Northern Ireland) (FoE)
26-28 Underwood Street
London N1 7JQ
℃ 071 490 1555
Works to promote policy changes that will protect and improve the natural environment and to affect government policies on the environment by direct lobbying and public education.

Friends of the Earth Scotland
70-72 Newhaven Road
Edinburgh EH6 5QG
℃ 031 554 9977
(See FoE - above)

Game Conservancy
Fordingbridge
Hampshire SP6 1EF
℃ 0425 652381
A research institute which also advises landowners and conservationists.

Greenpeace (UK)
Canonbury Villas
London N1 2PN
℃ 071 354 5100
Campaigns against abuse of the environment through direct non-violent action and lobbying.

The Hawk and Owl Trust
C/o Birds of Prey Section
Zoological Society of London
Regent's Park
London NW1 4RY
Conserves and encourages the study of birds of prey, especially those native to the UK.

International Tree Foundation
Sandy Lane
Crawley Down
West Sussex RH10 4HS
℃ 0342 712536
Worldwide tree planting and protection society.

Irish Wildbird Conservancy
Ruttledge House
8 Longford Place
Monkstown
Co. Dublin
℃ 010 3531 280 4322
Promotes study and conservation of wild birds in Ireland.

League Against Cruel Sports
83-87 Union Street
London SE1 1SG
℃ 071 403 6155
Campaigns politically against sports which cause suffering to wildlife.

Living Earth
The Old Laundry
Ossington Buildings
Moxon Street
London W1M 3JD
℃ 071 487 3661
Promotes conservation primarily through education.

London Ecology Centre
45 Shelton Street
London WC2H 9HJ
℡ 071 379 4324
An advisory body for many ecological groups.

London Wildlife Trust
80 York Way
London N1 9AG
℡ 071 278 6612
Protects the wildlife of Greater London and aims to promote greater awareness of the value of wildlife.

Lynx
PO Box 509
Great Dunmow
Essex CM6 1UH
℡ 0371 872016
Campaigns against the killing of wild and captive animals for their fur.

Mammal Society
C/o Department of Zoology
University of Bristol
Woodlands Road
Bristol BS8 1UG
℡ 0272 272300
Promotes the study and conservation of mammals.

Marine Biological Association of the United Kingdom (MBA)
The Plymouth Marine Laboratory
Citadel Hill
Plymouth
Devon PL1 2PB
℡ 0752 222772
Promotes scientific research that contributes to marine biological science; runs the Marine Pollution Information Centre.

Marine Conservation Society (MCS)
9 Gloucester Road
Ross-on-Wye
Herefordshire HR9 5BU
℡ 0989 66017
Campaigns to protect and conserve the wildlife of the coast and offshore waters.

Media Natura
21 Tower Street
London WC2H 9NS
℡ 071 240 4936
An initiative from the media industry to help stimulate interest in environmental issues and to publicize conservation problems.

The Monkey Sanctuary
Looe
Cornwall PL13 1NZ
℡ 0503 262532
Provides a home for a colony of grey woolly monkeys, offers advice about keeping monkeys in captivity and has a rehabilitation project to reintroduce the species in Amazonia.

National Birds of Prey Centre
Newent
Gloucestershire GL18 1JJ
℡ 0531 820286
Has a successful captive breeding collection of raptors and advises other zoos in the breeding of endangered species. Also makes people more aware of the need to conserve species of birds of prey.

National Federation of Badger Groups
7 London Road
Tetbury
Gloucestershire GL8 8JQ
℡ 0666 503419
Works for the protection, welfare and conservation of badgers.

National Federation of City Farms
AMF House
93 Whitby Road
Brislington
Bristol BS4 3QF
℡ 0272 719109
Promotes and supports inner city farms where organic and sustainable farming methods are used.
For details of farm sites, please send an SAE.

National Rivers Authority
Eastbury House
30-34 Albert Embankment
London SE1 7TL
℡ 071 820 0101
Watchdog with powers to oversee the protection and improvement of water quality and environment in the UK.

National Trust Volunteers Office
33 Sheep Street
Cirencester
Gloucestershire GL7 1QW
℡ 0285 651818
Organizes volunteer work, including working holidays.

National Trust for Scotland
5 Charlotte Square
Edinburgh EH2 4DU
℡ 031 226 5922
Works to preserve land and buildings of national interest or natural beauty in Scotland.

Otter Trust
Earsham
Nr Bungay
Suffolk NR35 2AF
℡ 0986 893470
Protects and conserves otters worldwide, especially the European otter.

Owl Study Group
The Nunnery
Nunnery Place
Thetford
Norfolk IP24 2PU
℡ 0842 750050
A forum for the exchange of ideas and knowledge for people interested in owls.

PANOS
9 White Lion Street
London N1 9PD
℡ 071 278 1111
Provides information on environmental issues mainly in the form of briefings to the press and non-governmental organizations worldwide.

Plantlife
Natural History Museum
Cromwell Road
London SW7
℡ 071 938 9111
Works for the protection of plants faced with extinction worldwide and in the UK, and helps recreate lost habitats.

Rare Breeds Survival Trust
National Agricultural Centre
Kenilworth
Warwickshire CV8 2LG
℡ 0203 696551
Aims to increase the numbers of rare breeds, keeps breeding registers, provides funds and holds practical workshops.

Reptile Protection Trust
College Gates
2 Deansway
Worcester WR1 2JD
℡ 0483 417550
Works for the protection and conservation of all reptiles.

Royal Air Force Ornithological Society
General Secretary,
Flt. Sgt. C J Sparks
RAF Signals Engineering
Establishment
RAF Henlow
Bedfordshire SG16 6DN
Aims to encourage birdwatching and the science of ornithology in the RAF, especially on MOD properties.

Royal Naval Birdwatching Society
Hon. Secretary and Treasurer
Col. P J S Smith RM (Ret'd)
19 Downlands Way
South Wonston
Winchester
Hampshire SO21 3HS
℡ 0962 885258
Promotes birdwatching and the science of ornithology in the Royal Navy.

Royal Society for Nature Conservation (RSNC)
The Wildlife Trusts Partnership
The Green
Witham Park
Waterside South
Lincoln LN5 7JR
℡ 0522 544400
The umbrella group for the many local and county-based nature conservation trusts.

Royal Society for the Prevention of Cruelty to Animals (RSPCA)
Causeway
Horsham
West Sussex RH12 1HG
℡ 0403 264181
Promotes kindness to animals and aims to prevent cruelty and suffering.

Royal Society for the Protection of Birds (RSPB)
The Lodge
Sandy
Bedfordshire SG19 2DL
℡ 0767 680551
Conserves and protects wild birds, promotes the appreciation of birds, manages nature reserves, conducts research, surveys and campaigns.

RSPB (Scotland)
17 Regent Terrace
Edinburgh EH7 5BN
℡ 031 557 3136
(See RSPB - above)

RSPB (Wales)
Bryn Aderyn
The Bank
Newtown
Powys SY16 2AB
℡ 0686 626678
(See RSPB - above)

Scott Polar Research Institute (SPRI)
Lenfield Road
Cambridge CB2 1ER
℡ 0223 336540
A large and very specialist research unit and information service covering all aspects of the polar regions.

Scottish Conservation Projects
Freepost
Stirling SK8 2BR
℡ 0786 79697
Scotland's leading charity involving people in improving the quality of their environment through practical conservation work.

Scottish Natural Heritage
12 Hope Terrace
Edinburgh EH9 2AS
℡ 031 447 4784
The new organization which replaced the Countryside Commission and Nature Conservancy Council in Scotland from April 1992.

Scottish Society for the Prevention of Cruelty to Animals
19 Melville Street
Edinburgh EH3 7PL
℡ 031 225 6418
Animal welfare charity dealing with wildlife, livestock and pets. Runs wildlife rehabilitation unit.

Scottish Tree Trust
30 Edgemont Street
Glasgow G41 3EL
℡ 041 649 2462
Works to maintain native woodlands.

Scottish Wildlife Trust
25 Johnstone Terrace
Edinburgh EH1 2NH
© 031 445 4198
Works to conserve Scotland's natural flora and fauna.

The Seabird Group
℅ RSPB
The Lodge
Sandy
Bedfordshire SG19 2DL
© 0767 680551
Concerned with the conservation of seabirds. Coordinates census and monitoring work on breeding seabirds.

Sea Shepherd
PO Box 5
Ashford
Middlesex
© 0784 254846
Campaigns to conserve and protect all marine wildlife.

Society of Wildlife Artists
Federation of British Artists
17 Carlton House Terrace
London SW1Y 5BD
© 071 930 6844
Annual exhibition of paintings in summer selected from an open submissions process. Membership by invitation only.

Tree Council
35 Belgrave Square
London SW1X 8QN
© 071 235 8854
Aims to improve the environment through the planting and care of trees.

Trust for Urban Ecology (TRUE)
PO Box 514
London SE16 1AS
© 071 237 9165
Aims to promote awareness and expertise in urban ecology, habitat creation and urban wildlife management.

Voluntary Service Overseas (VSO)
317 Putney Bridge Road
London SW15 2PN
© 081 780 1331
Organizes voluntary work worldwide.

Wader Study Group
44 The Pastures
Edlesborough
Dunstable
Bedfordshire LU6 2HL
An association of amateurs and professionals interested in wading birds.

Whale and Dolphin Conservation Society
19a James Street West
Bath
Avon BA1 2BT
© 0225 334511
Works for the conservation of whales and dolphins and promotes public awareness of their plight.

Wildfowl and Wetlands Centre
Martin Mere
Burscough
Ormskirk
Lancashire L40 0TA
© 0704 895181
A sanctuary for injured and orphaned birds.

Wildfowl and Wetlands Trust
Slimbridge
Gloucestershire GL2 7BT
© 0453 890333
Works to conserve and study wildfowl and their habitats.

Wildlife Hospitals Trust
St Tiggywinkles
Aston Road
Haddenham
Buckinghamshire HP17 8AF
© 0844 292292
Takes in and treats all species of British wild animal and bird. Educates others in the care and treatment of wild animals.

Wildlife Society
Alderbrook
Craven Road
Inkpen
Newbury
Berkshire RG1 0DX
Encourages the use of film and video to record and better understand the natural environment.

Wildlife Sound Recording Society
National Sound Archive
29 Exhibition Road
London SW7 2AS
© 071 589 6603
Provides help and advice on the practical aspects of recording wildlife sounds.

Women's Environmental Network
Aberdeen Studios
22 Highbury Grove
London N5 2EA
© 071 354 8823
Deals with various environmental problems that are of specific concern to women.

Woodlands Trust
Autumn Park
Dysart Road
Grantham
Lincolnshire NG31 6LL
© 0476 74297
Works for the conservation of broadleaved and native British trees and the creation and development of new woodlands.

Working Weekends on Organic Farms (WWOOF)
19 Bradford Road
Lewes
East Sussex BN7 1RB
Helps promote organic farming through the support of volunteers.

World of Water (WoW)
6 Fourth Avenue
Birmingham B29 7EU
© 021 472 7372
Aims to raise public awareness of the value of water and its ecological use.

World Wide Fund for Nature UK (WWF-UK)
Panda House
Weyside Park
Godalming
Surrey GU7 1XR
© 0483 426444
Campaigns to conserve natural resources and promote sustainable activity through education, public policy, site protection, training and the conservation of species.

Zoo Check
Coldharbour
Dorking
Surrey RH5 6HA
© 0306 712091
Monitors zoo conditions throughout the UK.

POLITICAL GROUPS

Green Alliance
60 Chandos Place
London WC2N 4HG
© 071 836 0341
Encourages ecological awareness through all political life in the UK.

Green Democrats (formerly Liberal Ecology Group)
19a Earls Court Square
London SW5 9BY
© 071 373 4631
Works to raise environmental and ecological issues within the party.

Green Party
10 Station Parade
Balham High Road
London SW12 9AZ
© 081 673 0045
Campaigns to promote harmony with nature and the practice of sustainable economic activity.

Tory Green Initiative
1 Margaret Street
London W1N 7LG
© 071 580 4433
Informs MPs and others of developments in the international ecology movement.

FOR CHILDREN

Go Wild Club
PO Box 101
Wetherby
Yorkshire LS23 6EE
© 0937 541542
Junior branch of the WWF for members aged 7-18.

Mammal Society Youth Group
℅ Department of Zoology
University of Bristol
Woodlands Road
Bristol BS8 1UG
© 0272 272300
Seeks to promote an interest in mammals, mainly for the under 18s.

Operation Raleigh
The Power House
Alpha Place
Flood Street
London SW3 5SZ
© 071 351 7541
An international charity which aims to develop the potential of people aged 17-25. It organizes conservation and community projects at home and abroad.

Watch Trust for Environmental Education Ltd (WATCH)
The Green
Witham Park
Waterside South
Lincoln LN2 2NR
© 0552 544400
Run by the RSNC to enable young people (up to 18 years) to increase their knowledge of wildlife and to take an active part in conservation.

Young People's Trust for the Environment & Nature Conservation
95 Woodbridge Road
Guildford
Surrey GU1 4PY
© 0483 39600
An education and information service, especially for schools, on nature conservation issues.

Young Ornithologists Club (YOC)
The Lodge
Sandy
Bedfordshire SG19 2DL
© 0767 680551
The junior branch of the RSPB. Applicants must be under the age of 16 to join, but can remain in the YOC until the age of 18.

VOLUNTEER WORK OPPORTUNITIES WITH WILDLIFE AND CONSERVATION ORGANIZATIONS

Organization	Overseas volunteers	Design and/or illustration	Committee work	Education (with adults and children)	Computers	Fundraising	Leafletting	Recording and surveying	Sales, stalls and fairs	Stewards and wardens	Administration/Office work	Communicating with the public	Campaigning	Practical conservation work	Education (Preparation of materials)	Guided walks	Professional skills	Speaking at lectures	Research
Amateur Entomologists Society										●					●				●
Ark Environmental Foundation			●	●	●	●						●	●	●		●		●	●
British Naturalists Association			●			●		●	●			●					●	●	●
British Trust for Conservation Volunteers												●		●	●				
British Trust for Ornithology		●			●	●		●	●				●		●	●	●	●	●
Butterfly Conservation Society					●	●		●	●						●			●	●
Care for the Wild								●										●	
Centre for Urban Ecology												●							
Common Ground												●						●	
Council for National Parks			●		●					●		●	●	●				●	●
Council for the Protection of Rural England						●	●		●			●	●	●					
Countryside Education Trust			●		●	●	●	●	●	●	●	●		●		●	●	●	●
Countryside Venture					●	●	●		●			●				●		●	●
Earthwatch (Europe)	●																		
Friends of the Earth	●	●			●	●	●					●				●		●	●
Gaia Foundation				●	●	●	●					●	●			●		●	●
Greenpeace						●				●		●							
Hawk and Owl Trust						●			●	●									
International Council for Bird Preservation	●	●			●							●						●	●
International Primate Protection League	●					●	●					●	●	●					
Living Earth			●	●	●	●	●					●				●		●	●
Marine Conservation Society			●			●		●	●			●						●	
Men of the Trees					●		●		●						●	●	●		●
National Trust for Scotland					●			●								●	●		
National Trust Volunteer Unit				●				●		●	●		●				●	●	●
Operation Raleigh	●	●	●	●	●	●	●	●	●	●	●	●	●	●	●	●		●	●
People's Trust for Endangered Species			●					●	●										
Plantlife								●	●			●				●			
Population Concern				●	●				●		●								●
Reptile Protection Trust				●	●	●			●			●							
Royal Society for Nature Conservation			●	●	●	●	●	●	●	●	●	●	●	●	●	●	●	●	●
Royal Society for the Prevention of Cruelty to Animals			●	●	●	●	●		●		●	●	●	●			●		●
Royal Society for the Protection of Birds										●			●	●					
Scottish Conservation Projects			●					●	●		●			●	●	●	●		●
Sea Shepherd			●			●	●		●		●		●	●					●
Trust for Urban Ecology			●		●	●		●	●		●	●	●		●	●		●	●
Voluntary Services Overseas	●																		
Wildlife Hospital Trust				●															
Women's Environmental Network			●		●	●	●	●		●		●	●	●		●		●	●
Woodland Trust											●								●
Working Weekends on Organic Farms												●							●
World of Water	●	●	●	●	●	●						●	●	●	●	●		●	●
World Wide Fund for Nature			●				●	●		●									
Zoo Check				●	●	●		●		●		●							

ACKNOWLEDGEMENTS

Jill Bailey *(MA Oxon)* has written over 40 children's books and several adult books. She has also written and produced videos for the BBC, some of which have won awards.

John Birdsall *(BSc)* is a freelance writer and editor specializing in wildlife and conservation topics.

Hanna Bolus *(MA Oxon)* is a freelance writer and editor on international environmental issues.

Duncan Brewer is a full-time writer whose specializations include natural history, earth sciences, Third World issues and investigative journalism.

Michael Bright is a managing editor with the BBC's world-renowned Natural History Unit in Bristol. He is the producer of numerous wildlife and conservation books, including his latest *The Private Life of Birds* to be published in 1993.

Helen Clapperton *(LLB)* is a trainee solicitor at Frere Cholmeley Solicitors, London. She has spent the last few months on secondment to the Foundation for International Environmental Law and Development, based at the School of Law, Kings College London, London University.

Mark Cocker *(BA)* is a professional author and naturalist.

Jonathan Elphick *(BSc)* is a natural history editor, consultant and author who has written regularly on birds for the *Wildlife Fact-File*.

Sarah Foster *(BA)* is a journalist with a special interest in the environment. She is also an experienced scuba diver and last winter spent five months in Central America, where she was involved in marine conservation work.

Jeff Hall is a writer, photographer, professional tour guide and whale researcher, working in Alaska, California, Baja California and the mountains and deserts of the southwestern USA.

Dr Tony Hare is an ecologist, businessman and communicator. He has produced numerous TV programmes, books and articles about the environment. He has worked with many wildlife and environmental organizations and is Chairman of the Board of Plantlife, the plant conservation charity.

John Hechtel is a specialist in bear behaviour, ecology and conservation who has worked for the Alaska Department of Fish and Game since 1980. He has been involved in research on bears for over 17 years, including brown (grizzly), black and polar bears. He is also a writer and photographer and has advised on television productions by both National Geographic and the BBC.

Suzanne Jones *(BA)* is a writer and editor who has recently been involved with the *Wildlife Fact-File*.

Dr R E Kenward *(BA, MA, DPhil, FLS)* was born into a farming family in 1949, then took Honours and Doctoral degrees at Oxford University and now studies birds of prey for the Institute of Terrestrial Ecology. With more than 50 scientific publications, including books on goshawks and radio-tagging, he is a Director-at-Large of the Raptor Research Foundation and a Fellow of the Linnean Society.

Fred Pearce is an environmental journalist and author specializing in international issues. He is an author of books on acid rain, the greenhouse effect and environmental campaigning.

Michael Scott *(BSc, Dip Ed)* is a writer and broadcaster on wildlife and conservation, who also edits and publishes *SCENES*, the Scottish Environmental Newsletter.

Nigel Sitwell edited *Wildlife* magazine (now renamed *BBC Wildlife*) for 16 years, and currently travels the world reporting on wildlife and the environment.

Tony Stones *(BSc, MSc)* trained as an ecologist and has worked for the Royal Society for the Protection of Birds as a freelance environmentalist, acting as the principal contributor to the publication *Important Bird Areas in the UK*.

Matthew Turner *(BA)* is a writer and editor who has recently contributed to the *Wildlife Fact-File*.

David Unwin studied pterosaurs for his PhD at Reading University and is now a Royal Society Research Fellow at Bristol University. At present he is working on fossil birds, baby ichthyosaurs and the wings of pterosaurs, the latter in conjunction with a Russian palaeontologist, N N Bakhurina, to whom he is married. Next year he plans to search for dinosaurs and pterosaurs in Western Mongolia.

Jeremy West is a professional sound recordist, who specializes in wildlife and natural history recordings as well as the live soundtrack for adventure documentary films.

PICTURE CREDITS

Abbreviations:
t – top; b – bottom; l – left; r – right

Animals Animals/Earth Scenes M Dick 28

Ardea London Ltd 114b; B Y Arthus 190b; I Beames 103tl; R Bunge 66br; J Daniels 52b; J P Ferrero 19br, 97; B Gibbons 117bl, 149t; F Gohier 32b, 35t, 106tl, 123b, 182t; C Haagner 99br; P Morris 105br, 171t; E Parer-Cook 11tl, 119, 158–159, 171b; J Player 50; R Vaughan 102

David Robert Austen 93, 96bl, 98

R Barnwell 186tl, 189t

Bavarian State Collection 54t

P Bloom 183 br

Bluwater Golf Products 185br

Bruce Coleman Ltd 29t; J & D Bartlett 166tr; H Brehm 131; A Compost 26b; M Fogden 67tl, 124b; J Foott 2–3, 19tl, 35b; M Freeman 52tl, 82b; C B Frith 24, 25; Frithfoto 27t; F Futil 143b; S Krasemann 16tl; J Langsbury 91br, 130tl; F Lanting 117tr; L C Marigo 126tl; G McCarthy 134t; J Murray 73br; D & M Plage 110; H Reinhard 11tr, 132t; K Taylor 45, 47t, 192; U Walz 61; R Williams 63t, 76b, 125, 128b, 144, 145b, 189br; G Zeisler 38, 42t, 44t

Martyn Cowley 56b

Daniel J Cox 12tl, 13, 14bl, 15tr, 18bl, 161tl

Earthwatch Europe M Christie 69tr; A Schreeber 109t; Smith 123tl

Victor Englebert 94t, 95b

English Nature 146, P Wakely 149b

Mary Evans Picture Library 178bl, 179tr

Frank Lane Picture Agency H Clark 135; D Grewcock 113br; J Hawkins 151br; P Heard 37; E & D Hosking 51tr, 91t, 108tl, 161b, 191br; F Polking 115; Silvestris 21, 67br; W Wisniewski 186b.

A D Goodson 182b

Greenpeace 155tr; Dom 157b4; Dorreboon 153; Franks 157b1; Leitinger 155b; Morgan 152tl, 152bl, 156b; Morris 154; Olsen 157b2; Pahlich 157b3; Van de Bunt 156tl

John Hechtel 16br

The Image Bank Artphotopolke 75; De Moura Machado 112; S Wilkinson 157tl

JNCC S Moore 150

JWPT J Hartley 170, 173br; P Trenchard 161tr, 168tl; W R Wood 169

The Mansell Collection 179tl

David M Martill 58t, 59br

B McConnell 185tl

MCS 136tl

Nature Photographers Ltd P Sterry 100l; W S Paton 60b; R Tidman 85tr

The Natural History Museum, London 175, 177br, 178tr, 176br, 174bl, 177tr, 176tl, 179b, 174tl, 178tl

NHPA ANT 22; H Ausloos 142; A Bannister 163, 164br, 166bl; B Beehler 29b; G I Bernard 23b; N Callow 104bl; G Cambridge 20tl; L Campbell 167br; D Currey 142tr; S Dalton 20b, 40tl, 41, 46, 64, 105tl, 111b; B Hawkes 188; H Ingen 96tr; S Krasemann 14t; T McDonald 82t; H Palo 114tl, 120–121; J Sauvanet 23t; J Shaw 17t; K Switak 116

Natural Science Photos C Blaney 88tl; J C Pasieka 145t; R Revels 90t; P Ward 60t

Oxford Scientific Films A Bannister 92bl; D Fox 51b; H Hall 118; M Hamblin 62; A MacEwen 6; G A Maclean 63b; OSF/Okapia A Shah 107; S Osolinski 123tr; S Pilkington 70–71; R Pockwood 88bl; A Shay 53b; K Westerskov 85b, 86bl, 87br, 136b

Pembrokeshire Coast National Park T Thomas 147

Planet Earth Pictures S Avery 172; D Barrett 84; M Clay 66tl, 148; R Coomber 36b; G Douwma 43b, 137; J Downer 39t; G du Feu 181; C Farnetti 44b; P Folkens 30; H Heap 49; C Howes 90 bl; K Lukas 184br; J Lythgoe 73bl, 95tr; D Maitland 81tl, 138; M Mattock 36tl, 101; D Perrine 11b, 180b; D A Ponton 113tl; K Puttock 4; T Risi 139tl; D E Romley 129br; K Scholey 86t, 103br; J Scott 47b, 190t, 108br, 111t, 165tr, 187; N Sefton 140bl; H Voigtmann 80

Rex Features Ltd Keystone 79t

RSPB 130bl; M Edwards 133b; C H Gomersall 132br, 134b

Kevin Schafer & Martha Hill Photographers © K Schafer 8, 79b, 124tl, 127tr, 127bl, 128tr, 129l

SMRU 184 tl

Science Photo Library M Dohrn/S Winkworth 57t; J Yeats 89

Spooner/Gamma R Gaillard R. 65, 68, 69bl; A Ribeiro 74tl

Still Pictures D Dancer 78; M Edwards 73t, 76, 77, 81b

Streano/Havens © V Streano 31, 33t, 33b, 34b

Survival Anglia Ltd R Price 141

Dr P M Thompson 180tl

Tom Stack & Associates M Nilsen 83; T Tackett 99tl

Neil Turner 7tr

VIREO A Morris 39b J West 162tl, 164tl

Zefa Picture Library T van Sant/Geosphere Project Endpapers

INDEX